THE NHS AN...

BOOKLET 2

CUSTOMER FEEDBACK SURVEYS: an introduction to survey methods

THE AUTHORS

Paul Dixon was until recently Convenor of Sociological Methods teaching at the University of Sussex. He is now a freelance social researcher.
Roy Carr-Hill is ESRC Senior Research Fellow at the Centre for Health Economics at the University of York.

This booklet is one of a series reporting on a study "The NHS and Its Customers," funded by the Department of Health.

FURTHER COPIES

Further copies of this single booklet are available at price £3.50 to cover the costs of publication postage and packing from:

The Secretary
Centre for Health Economics,
University of York,
Heslington,
York, YO1 5DD.
Tel: 0904 433648/433646

The complete set of three booklets plus the executive summary is available at the price of £7.50. Please make cheques payable to University of York.

THE NHS AND ITS CUSTOMERS

BOOKLET 2

CUSTOMER FEEDBACK SURVEYS: an introduction
to survey methods

Paul Dixon
and
Roy Carr-Hill

January 1989

Published by
The Centre for Health Economics
University of York
Heslington
York YO1 5DD

Laserset by Computype, 241 Hull Road, York YO1 3LA.
Printed by J.W. Bullivant & Son, 296 Bishopthorpe Road, York YO2 1LG.

TABLE OF CONTENTS

ACKNOWLEDGEMENTS

We would like to thank all Health Authorities and CHCs who kindly provided the studies for the review, and whose experiences heavily informed this guidebook. We would also like to thank members of the "Management Peer Review Group" for their help at various stages, and those at the Centre for Health Economics and Department of Health, who made comments on draft versions of the text.

In addition we would like to record our thanks for the valuable contributions made by the secretaries Sal Cuthbert, Vanessa Windass, Paula Press and Vanessa Waby, and those who helped us carry out the research, Sharon Dexter, Sheila Jefferson, Elaine Smedley and Robert Sin.

INTRODUCTION

This guidebook is intended for the budding practitioner, the person (or persons) designated to look after customer relations (or quality assurance), who appreciates the potential value of surveys but is unsure how to start. It is not, however, a textbook to be learnt from beginning to end: it should be dipped into. To assist the reader in consulting the guide, a "flow chart" of the survey process is described in Chapter 1 indicating the appropriate chapters or sections of chapters, as well as a detailed table of contents.

Our reader is the person or team entrusted by management with the task of finding out what the customer or potential customer thinks of the NHS in a particular locality. This may, of course, include a wide variety of possible target customers. Whilst the general advice and approach is appropriate for all surveys in the health care area, the booklet does not deal in any detail with the particular problems raised by the circumstances and conditions of specific groups; nor does it pretend to offer an adequate coverage of the issues involved in carrying out a general population audit. More specific advice will be found in the accompanying booklet *A Review of Studies,* which evaluates the methods of several hundred surveys, highlights examples of good practice, and gives details of how, and how not, to do particular types of survey.

1. WHEN NOT TO DO A SURVEY

This introductory chapter is divided into two parts. The first warns you off doing surveys when the information can equally well be obtained from other sources. The second provides a flow chart of how to go about a survey.

§1.1 WHEN NOT TO DO A SURVEY

1.1 Even quite small surveys can be expensive in time, money and other resources. Surveys which fail also incur other costs—they may have inspired false hopes or opened up issues which are better kept closed.

1.2 The review of surveys in booklet III shows that there are often methodological reasons why surveys fail to produce the hoped for results. Careful design and preliminary checks should help avoid such failures.

Pitfalls

1.3 Even the most conclusive of surveys is wasted if the report is unread: the proposals rejected or quietly filed. Ensuring that the style, length and presentation of the report matches the intended readership is one important factor, but if local conditions are unfavourable, it may not be worth starting a survey. Experience suggests that surveys are unlikely to succeed if:

- the research has not previously been agreed with relevant staff; or they are likely to oppose the eventual proposals;

- the group doing the research has no access to decisional processes, has low status, or has been otherwise marginalised;
- there are likely to be no resources to implement proposals.
- there are insufficient technical and staff resources to effectively conduct the research, especially the analysis and reporting stages;
- the time-scale is too tight;
- the data is likely to be inconclusive and no proposals will result;
- the data, or a near equivalent, is already available from official sources or other studies.

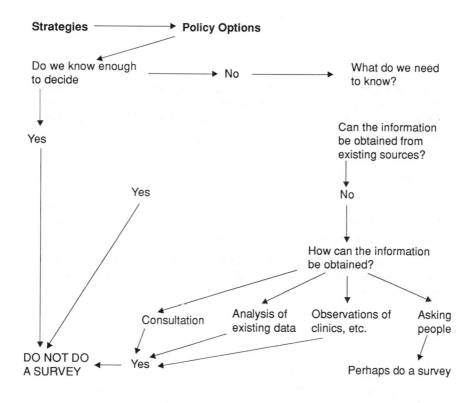

When not to do a survey

§1.2 ALTERNATIVES TO SURVEYS

1.4 One unfortunate consequence of concentrating on the details of survey technique is the tendency to devalue less formal and less technical research methods. In academic work, formal methods are used, if at all, at a late stage in the research, after various sorts of exploratory studies. Obviously there are times when quantitative data collected by formal methods is essential, but units should become more aware of the informal data collection that may already be part of their daily routine.

Informal Data Sources

1.5 Customer opinions are registered in a variety of fora, such as magazines and radio phone-ins, and managers could profit from them even though they are likely to represent the more vocal end of the spectrum. Even in the hospital context, the traditional complaints box is not the only method of tapping patient opinion: some hospitals have made special telephone lines available, or instituted a system of wishing lists. The matron rounds and ward meetings are other opportunities to hear the patient; and more effort can be made to ask family and friends what they think.

1.6 In some circumstances, it is worth investigating the possibility of ensuring that these observations and conversations are systematically reported. It often makes more sense to extend these informal methods, rather than conduct an expensive and potentially inconclusive survey.

Drawbacks of formal methods

1.7 Expense and inconclusive results are not the only reasons for exploring alternatives. One of the great assets of survey research, people's considerable willingness to fill in self-completion questionnaires, hides one of its main drawbacks: that you only get their replies to a series of pre-set questions, not their spontaneous views. Once the fieldwork is over, there is a considerable temptation to forget that what you are confidently describing as your respondents' views are only their replies to *your* questions, and not necessarily *their* own interests and priorities. If health service policy has been steered by providers' perceptions and definitions of good practice, should this also hold for consumer research? If one is to emphasise the patients' agenda, how should this be done?

3

§1.3 CRITICAL INCIDENT ANALYSIS

1.8 Critical Incident Analysis is an approach which tries to discover both the patients' agenda and their definitions of good practice. Based on methods used in fields as diverse as operational research and phenomenological sociology, it centres on patients reconstructing what amounts to a diary of their hospital or other care experiences. It asks them to report what was important, notable, strange, and worrying—anything which stood out in their memory, from the friendliness of the porter who guided them past incoherent signposting, to the anxieties of being left sitting alone on a bed in a ward.

Example of Use of CIA

1.9 N.W. Thames RHA has used this method quite extensively and produced an excellent manual (N.W. Thames [1986A]) showing how it can be applied to out-patient research. Their interviews start by asking how the appointment was made; whether these arrangements were what patients expected; and whether there was anything they especially liked or disliked about the process. They go on on to ask about travel to the clinic and the reception process, right through to the arrangements for getting home. Patients are asked what actually happened at each stage, whether this was what they expected, and whether they found anything especially good or bad. The interviews are focused in taking interviewees through all these stages; and at times quite directive, when, for example respondents are prompted for their opinions on signposting, queuing and refreshment facilities. The aim was not only to record these opinions, but to get some sense of those aspects which were most important to the patients.

1.10 Contrast this with the sort of general self-completion questionnaire which gets patient opinion on a wide range of topics and assumes those which score lowest are those requiring most attention. Less focused forms of CIA may be appropriate in other circumstances, e.g. in investigating the routine experiences of long-stay in-patients. After a number of such interviews, one should be able to identify the main concerns of various groups of patients and what they would like by way of improvements. This information may be useful in its own right, and form the basis for policy (see e.g. N.W. Thames [1986B & C]), or it may be used to develop cheaper and more easily used research tools, such as self-completion questionnaires (e.g. E. Dorset [1987]).

Why Use CIA

1.11 As the N.W. Thames group freely admit, this is neither the quickest nor cheapest way of collecting information from patients. It needs trained interviewers and collects data whose analysis may be both difficult and time consuming.

Difficulties are heightened if one finds several distinct patterns of responses and these need to be clearly delineated and explained. Nor is it a particularly "safe" form of research, having the potential to disrupt established agendas. Nevertheless, this is a technique worth considering, especially if there is a growing discrepancy between staff reports of patient opinion and results from self-completion surveys. The benefits could be considerable, and potential users can take some comfort, as well as guidance, from the N.W. Thames work, which found that patients' concerns could be translated into manageable policy. It may be too costly and time-consuming to regularly repeat, but could be an occasional substitute for a general opinion survey.

§1.4 DOING A SURVEY

Objectives	Read Section	Comments
Are these clear and potentially answerable by survey?	§2.1	*If not, return to peer group who suggested survey – DO NOT PROCEED.*
Specify precise aims of survey	§2.1–2	*If not, return to objectives*
Propose rough timetable	ch.9	

Preliminaries		
What do we already know about the situation?	–	*If enough is known to formulate policy,* WHY A SURVEY?
Look at reports of similar studies	**Booklet III**	
Pre-piloting, finding out which kinds of questions will be appropriate	**Booklet III & ch.2**	*If this is not done, statistics won't save you*
Draw up a sampling plan	**ch.3**	
Will any of these analyses require technical input?	**ch.10**	

Preliminaries cont.	Read	Comments
Survey Design to include:		
• whether interview or self-completion	§5.1	
• sampling plan and rough size of sample (this might be as simple as a choice of clinics and a number of days)	ch.3	
• length and style of questionnaire	ch.4	
• proposed staff and training	§5.2–3 & ch.9	
• plan for fieldwork (crucially proposed dates, times and proposed location of staff)	ch.9	
• preparations for coding, data entry	ch.7	
• plan for analysis	ch.8	
• rough timetable for survey	ch.9	
Seeking agreement on sampling points from floor management	**Booklet III**	
Re-examine design of survey for technical inputs		*If you will need statistical/technical advice, get it **now***
Questionnaire Design		
Produce first draft of questionnaire. Circulate to interested parties. Try it on friends	ch.4	*Remember the potential respondents are at best patient, probably long-suffering, and may not read or speak English fluently. Don't make it worse by asking them to answer an incomprehensible question*

Questionnaire design cont.	Read	Comments
Piloting, trying out the draft questionnaire on a small number of the potential respondents	–	
Analyse the responses from the pilot	ch.8	*If it looks as if you won't get the answers you need, DO NOT PROCEED*
Final approval from colleagues	–	*Return to examine aims of research and whether design is appropriate*
Setting Up		
Choosing staff for interviewing	§5.2–3	*Good interviewers are rare; they need to be insistent but extremely pleasant with it*
Choosing staff for clerical work	§7.6–8	*Although much of work is clerical, accuracy is obviously very important*
Finalise fieldwork plan (dates, times and location of staff)		
Preparation of interviewers		
Execution		
Data Collection		*Regular spot visits by you to see how things are going*
Running record of progress		*Compare with sampling plan*
Coding and data entry	ch.7	*If possible, arrange for checking*

Execution cont.	Read	Comments
Analysis	ch.8	*Refer repeatedly to original aims of survey*
Report writing		
Discuss proposed draft with peer group and management		
Formal report for action		
Monitor effectiveness	§2.5	

2. ESSENTIAL PRELIMINARIES

This chapter looks at:

- the problems of designing a survey and defining your objectives
- various types of survey design, from "snapshot," to continuous monitoring
- how much attention should be paid to questions of method
- basic issues in monitoring research and assessing its effectiveness

§2.1 GETTING YOUR OBJECTIVES CLEAR: WHAT DO YOU WANT TO FIND OUT?

2.1 Information—and consumer feedback is no exception—is only useful when your objectives are clear. Many of the studies reviewed in the next booklet fail to reach tangible conclusions simply because they fail to define their aims beyond "wanting to find out about conditions . . . in . . ." and because they had failed to work out how the data they were collecting could be turned into policy proposals. The difficulties of using a general purpose questionnaire to reach policy relevant conclusions/recommendations should not be underestimated.

2.2 In the first place, with most surveys, the results are broadly predictable. They are unlikely to tell you anything new, only to support your own observations with quantitative data. Secondly, very little can be done with absolute percentages. Suppose you find satisfaction levels between 70% and 80%, does this mean things are going well or badly? Are these results better, or worse than those obtained with different questions elsewhere?

The Need for Comparisons

2.3 Answering these questions requires comparative data. This could come from the same study—when you might be comparing results from several different units: or from previous studies done either in your Authority or elsewhere. Without such comparisons, the results are difficult to interpret.

2.4 The need for comparisons raises two further points. First, that there should be greater standardisation in the questions asked. Second that it is difficult to make effective comparisons with results from weak questions—i.e. when the wording tends to get the same response from most informants.

2.5 Finally, even if percentage differences show that some services are less well thought of than others, they do not tell you precisely *what* is disliked or what patients would like done as a remedy. There are two ways of finding this out—you can either ask many specific questions, hoping that one of these covers the source of dissatisfaction; or you can ask for patients' comments—perhaps with a question such as "What did they dislike most"—or a probe to ask why they said "NO" to a particular pre-coded question.

Including Open Comments

2.6 When studies were able to make detailed and specific recommendations, it was noticeable that these were rarely inspired by the percentage differences, but by the open comments. If you only collect pre-coded data of a rather general kind, expect to have to do further, and more investigative work, to identify the source of discontent in the areas of lowest satisfaction. Identifying what data needs collecting, and how it will be used is a major part of drawing up a detailed specification and statement of aims.

2.7 Whether or not this is done, the potential effectiveness of a survey should be tested by running a trial analysis on your pilot data and checking that it is capable of informing the sort of recommendations you want.

What can be learned

2.8 It is important to emphasise that there is no such thing as a perfect piece of research. Whilst researchers in an academic context will frequently end their report with a plea for further research, they also typically draw attention to how much can be learnt by their approach. The latter is the more appropriate emphasis in this context.

2.9 The point is to recognise the often fragile information base for present policies; and therefore to realise the scope for improvement. Whilst this does not mean that *any* information is better than none, it does mean that a wide variety of approaches to collecting information will provide a useful addition to what is known.

§2.2. "RESEARCH" AND "ACADEMIC" CRITERIA

2.10 So you have decided to do a survey. How important is it to observe the technical criteria—what the 'research methodologist' says you should do? There is a tendency for authors to distance themselves from 'research'. The award-winning Oldchurch Hospital survey (Barking et al, 83) opens with the comment:

> "It should be stressed that the study was *not* a research project but was initiated to provide local management with a 'picture' of the role of the A & E department in order to rectify any major deficiencies in service."

2.11 Many other feedback surveys, with painstaking methods and high response rates, are equally self-deprecating. The most frequent remark is that a study, which uses a perfectly valid cross-sectional design, is "only a snapshot." Such self-criticism seems to be founded first on the belief that a study is not proper research unless it rests on some sort of hypothesis. And, secondly on the assumption that a survey is diminished unless it uses conspicuously technical methods. As the next few sub-sections hope to show, both are generally unfounded.

2.12 On the other hand, this tendency to regard feedback studies as something different from *real* research can produce a sort of cavalier disregard for basic principles. The following argument is typical:

> "What if my response rate is only 30%? Most local councillors get elected on a lower percentage, and I still have 400 replies?"

2.13 The notion that one set of criteria applies to health service surveys and another for academic research is unsound. Health surveys may have to pay more attention to questions of effectiveness—and may be more descriptive than hypothesis testing, but they still can benefit from good design. A survey which has only a 30% response rate will have expended considerable resources trying unsuccessfully to reach the other 70%; it will have no way of telling whether policy based on the views of that particular minority is likely to be acceptable to the other 70%—though one suspects that with such a low response rate, certain groups will be systematically under-represented. One should automatically be suspicious of a questionnaire giving such low response rates—were its questions so incoherent or irrelevant that so many respondents gave up? One could also argue that a

11

pre-condition of any serious patient feedback exercise is that it should record the views of more than this small proportion.

2.14 There are some very technical forms of data analysis and accuracy estimation which are unlikely to be relevant to most feedback studies, but the vast majority of methodological criteria, which are sometimes dismissed as "academic," are really only ways of ensuring conclusive and cost effective surveys.

§2.3. RESEARCH AIMS

2.15 Surveys will normally have one or more of the following objectives:

(a) *Explanatory studies*
These would usually be the first stage of any research where one is uncertain of the issues. They can include literature searches, and interviews with "experts" and others in the area. Jahoda et al gives a useful account of suitable methods. Exploratory studies may either be a preliminary to developing more formal methods, such as a pre-coded questionnaire, or may be worthwhile exercises in themselves in developing knowledge of a little known area.

(b) *Descriptive studies*
These are the type most often used in patient feedback studies. Their aim is usually to collect data which can influence or evaluate policy. Although descriptive, they should still have well-defined objectives—i.e. one should be precisely sure what range of data is needed and how it might lead to specific recommendations.

(c) *Hypothesis testing surveys*
These are widely used in socio-medical research. A typical study might aim to explore links between dietary patterns and a particular medical condition. They differ in two main respects from the descriptive model—though both are only differences of degree. First, their sampling strategy will require some sort of control group. Secondly, their analysis is unlikely to stop at basic frequency counts and cross-tabulations—and will include various forms of correlational analyses.

2.16 Hypothesis testing is not unknown in patient feedback research, especially when the project sets out to test the effects of a specific change—but it is less common than the descriptive type.

(d) *Other motives*

2.17 Finally, there are a variety of studies for which data collection is a secondary aim. Their intentions differ, but are usually either some form of public relations, or some attempt to demonstrate research activity (see Chapter 1 for reasons why surveys may not be the best way of meeting these objectives).

§2.4. RESEARCH DESIGN

2.18 Studies described as "snapshots" are frequently examples of cross-sectional designs. They are the most common form of feedback research, though one also finds examples of panel, quasi panel and standing panel models, and there is a well known experiment in continuous monitoring by CASPE in Bloomsbury HA.

Cross-sectional studies

2.19 These are simply surveys conducted at a single point in time. If they aim to be explanatory or test some hypothesis, they may well require a control group. If they are mainly descriptive, a control may not be necessary.

2.20 There is no reason why a cross-sectional study should not be valid or "scientific" provided the time chosen is not highly unrepresentative—such as an in-patient feedback study on Christmas Day.

Panel (or longitudinal) studies

2.21 These are ones in which informants are contacted more than once to find if they, their experiences and opinions, have changed over time. Perhaps the most famous British panel studies are the birth cohort studies conducted on large samples of all children born in single weeks in 1946, 1958 and 1970.

2.22 Longitudinal designs are well established in maternity studies, in which mothers report on the care received at different stages both before and after birth. They have also been used to evaluate after-care provided for elderly in-patients.

2.23 The simplest panel design interviews an individual both before and after a course of treatment. A less reputable version, the "quasi-panel" design compares the responses from a current *before* group with those of an *after* group, as if the two were identical. Though not normally providing valid comparisons, and therefore not recommended, the quasi-panel method is well-established (see e.g. Willmott and Young, 1957).

2.24 In a standing panel study, you keep in touch with a group of people to regularly ask their opinions. West Birmingham CHC kept a standing panel of elderly informants to get regular feedback on their experiences of the local health services. They seem to have under used the opportunity and the exercise is largely unreported, but in principle it is a method which ought to be more widely adopted. It could be a particularly useful way of getting regular information from health service users during periods of structural change.

Continuous monitoring

2.25 Continuous monitoring of patient opinion can take a variety of forms from periodically conducting cross-sectional surveys, to trying to get every patient admitted or discharged to fill in a questionnaire.

Example—CASPE in Bloomsbury

The major example in Britain of continuous monitoring is the CASPE (Clinical Accountability, Service, Planning and Evaluation) project being carried out in Bloomsbury health authority funded by the DHSS. The project is described in detail in Kerruish et al, 1988; here we provide only a brief summary and some notes to other health authorities which may not have Bloomsbury's capacity to adsorb the information produced.

Like many innovative experiments in continuous monitoring, the CASPE team are concentrating on developing the means both for rapidly and routinely collecting and handling data, and on methods for automatically analysing and interpreting the results for presentation to management at regular intervals.

Pilot data from over 3000 patients enabled the CASPE team to identify 15 basic areas of patient concern, and build these into a machine-readable questionnaire. This is now being used extensively at UCH and, with some additional questions, is being piloted at other establishments in the Bloomsbury HA. Results are presented to management on a monthly basis, as a series of easily readable indices evaluating different aspects of the scheme.

BLOOMSBURY HEALTH AUTHORITY

Bloomsbury Health Authority want to know how satisfied patients are with their care in hospital. Could you please help us by completing this questionnaire? Look for the box under the face which best expresses your views and fill in the white space as shown in the example:

EXAMPLE:

Your answers are not seen by staff caring for you; they are read directly by a machine so it is best to use either a pencil or a blue pen. We would welcome any additional comments, but could you please write them on a separate piece of paper.

	very satisfied 4	satisfied 3	somewhat dissatisfied 2	very dissatisfied 1

WHAT DO YOU THINK ABOUT THE FOLLOWING:

doctors

nurses

the clinical treatment you receive

the information that is given to you about your treatment

the control of any pain

atmosphere on the ward

noise on the ward

your surroundings (layout, furnishings, decor, etc.)

ward cleanliness

the way your day is organised on the ward

2.26 There are powerful arguments for such an approach. Proponents stress the potential speed of responses—management can immediately see how services are performing from the daily or weekly movement of the indices which provide a convenient way of continuously assessing patient reaction to any changes in the services. Thresholds can be set, so that intervention is automatically recommended when patient satisfaction levels fall below pre-determined standards (see Green, 1988)

Words of warning

2.27 There are however some caveats which ought to be extended. The range and type of data which can be collected by machine-readable questionnaire is obviously quite limited. Equipment set-up costs will be relatively high. And, apart from analytical objections to the widespread use of indices (see section §8.5), monitoring movements in this way is only useful if management are prepared to commit the resources to discovering the causes of any decline in satisfaction levels. There is also a presumption that the existing management and decision-making processes are ready for this continuous battery of index numbers, when some authorities seem unable, or sometimes unwilling?, to respond to results from the occasional one-off survey.

2.28 No one survey method is perfect. Almost any routine method is likely to provide only the most formal sorts of feedback based on the providers not the patients' agenda. Other methods—such as patient advocates, more regular management contacts with patients—might provide cheaper, more democratic, and more effective forms of feedback and an authority would certainly be advised to improve these channels in any case.

§2.5 THE IMPORTANCE OF MONITORING RESEARCH

2.29 We have emphasised that a well designed survey is not an end in itself: it is intended to influence policy. How do we know whether or not this has happened? If we fail to find out, how do we know whether the survey was, *in fact*, well-designed.

2.30 In a medical context, we might be used to carrying out—or at least receiving a report upon—a randomised controlled trial. In the case of assessing the effectiveness of research, life is much more difficult. For, in contrast to the RCT where both context and level of intervention are controlled, the consumer survey is moving through dark waters. Objectives change, the personnel change and practices change: *none* of the conditions for an RCT are available.

Assessing Effectiveness

2.31 In certain, very specific circumstances, it might be possible to carry out a repeat survey which could detect whether any of the observed changes were due to the policy recommendations implemented as a result of the first survey. More frequently, the survey—perhaps seen as completely appropriate then—is irrelevant now; new staff see the purposes and utility of the survey somewhat differently; and the organisational context to which the survey referred has also changed.

2.32 The point is that whilst it is relatively easy to describe what counts as a good, methodologically sound survey, it is usually much more difficult to choose simple criteria for what counts as a good survey in terms of the impact of the recommendation.

2.33 This does not mean that we have to renounce all efforts to evaluate the impact of the feedback exercise/research that has been carried out, but that any follow up has to be very sensitive to these changes in circumstance. The design of a follow-up/monitoring exercise has to be less like an RCT and more like a fieldwork trip for an anthropologist. What were the goals held by those commissioning the survey, carrying out the survey and those who agreed—or refused—to answer the questions? Whose policy agenda was incorporated into the design of the survey—either via the questionnaire itself or via the approach to the choice of samples or via the approach to respondents? Who has coded and analysed the responses according to a framework designed by whom? To whom were these results to be reported? Who—if anyone—was responsible for acting on the basis of the policy recommendations?

SUMMARY

Chapter 2 has:

- **stressed the need for clear objectives, a survey should not be started without them;**
- **described types of survey such as panel studies and continuous monitoring, other than the normal snapshot**
- **emphasised that surveys are by no means the only method of getting customer feedback**
- **underlined the need to pay attention to questions of method; a survey is worse than useless if it has very low response rates or otherwise unusable results**
- **recommended that all feedback surveys continually assess their own progress and try to anticipate their possible effectiveness.**

3. SAMPLING

This section covers:

- **What size sample will you need;**
- **How to improve the efficiency of a sample by stratifying or clustering;**
- **When to use quota samples;**
- **How to sample from lists and proxy lists;**
- **Pitfalls in using the Register of Electors;**
- **Testing if your sample is biased;**
- **Strategies for avoiding bias.**

§3.1. SAMPLING VS. CENSUSES

3.1 Surveys cost money, and the amount they cost varies in almost direct proportion to the number of people they try to contact. Few researchers have the resources to conduct a census i.e. attempt to get data from all individuals or households, though this is sometimes possible when researching small, well-defined, communities with relatively cheap methods such as self-completion questionnaires. (E.g. Seaton Sluice..) Normal practice is to draw a sample—i.e. select a group who will be representative of all those you wanted to contact.

3.2 There are four crucial issues

- **how many people do you need**
- **how to design your sample**
- **how do you identify and find your target group**
- **how to make sure those actually contacted are representative of the target group**

§3.2. WHAT SIZE SAMPLE

3.3 The rule of thumb in many health authority surveys is to draw as large a sample as can be afforded. This is not always good practice. It can encourage over-large samples and divert attention away from the real purpose of sampling—selecting respondents who are most relevant to the research issues.

Can a sample be too large?

3.4 Theoretically no, the larger a sample, the more accurate will be the results. But the law of diminishing returns applies, and the rate of increase in accuracy decreases with increasing size. More simply, if a sample of 50 patients all agree that the ward staff are excellent, but the toilet facilities and admission arrangements have definite faults, what is to be gained by having a much larger sample saying the same? This introduces an important and complicating factor in sample design—that the sample size needs to take account of the variation in the data. The more varied the responses, the larger the sample to get an equivalent level of accuracy.

What size sample to get within 5% of the true value? Statistical ways of estimating sample size.

3.5 Statistical formulae, often of mind-boggling complexity, can be used to predict what size of sample will be needed to achieve a specified level of accuracy.

3.6 Say we are trying to estimate what sample size would be needed to provide a value within 5% of the true (population) figure for a question such as

Were there enough bathrooms? YES/NO

The equation to give the required sample size will be:

$$1.96 \sqrt{\frac{PQ}{n}} < 5$$

where P is the average % saying YES to the question and Q is the average saying NO (i.e. 100-P). If previous surveys suggest that the proportion saying "YES" is likely to be around 70%, then the sample size is given by:

$$n > \frac{1.96^2}{25} \times 70(100-70) > 323$$

3.7 This formula is based on the theoretically simplest sort of sample—randomly drawing names from a list, with the further assumption that the potential population is so large that the list will not be significantly diminished each time a name is drawn.

3.8 Unfortunately, even here the situation is not as simple as it appears. Even though a sample is drawn perfectly randomly, it is still possible, though unlikely, that it consists of individuals whose views differ significantly from the norm. It is fundamental to the nature of sampling that we cannot definitively state that the result from single sample lies within a given % of the true value. We can only say that there is a calculable probability of it falling in this range. In this case, as well as requiring the value to be within 5% of the population figure, the multiplier "1.96" has been used to set at 95% the probability with which that occurs. That is, if we repeatedly drew samples of 323, we could say that in each case there is a 95% probability that the response of the sample, on this question, will be within 5% of the population value. Both conditions are quite severe; it would be an unusual social survey which set a range as tight as 5% and a probability as high as 95. The following table gives the ranges of values which are likely to occur with a probability of 68% in various sized samples on questions whose population figures are 52, 70 and 90%.

Sample size	Presumed proportions in Population					
	52%		70%		90%	
	s.e.	range+	s.e.	range+	s.e.	range+
50	7.1	44.9–59.1	6.5	63.5–76.5	4.2	85.8–94.2
100	5.0	47.0–57.0	4.6	65.4–74.6	3.0	87.0–94.2
200	3.5	48.5–55.5	3.2	66.8–73.2	2.1	87.9–92.1
300	2.9	49.1–54.9	2.6	67.4–72.6	1.7	88.3–91.7
400	2.5	49.5–54.5	2.3	67.7–72.3	1.5	88.5–91.5
500	2.2	49.8–54.2	2.0	68.0–72.0	1.3	88.7–91.3
700	1.9	50.1–53.9	1.7	68.3–71.7	1.1	88.9–90.1
1000	1.6	50.4–53.6	1.4	68.6–71.4	.95	89.1–91.9

+ Probability of your sample value falling within this range is 68%.

Accuracy and Sample Size

3.9 For example suppose our question theoretically elicits a 70% "YES" response from the entire patient population and we draw successive samples of 200. In around 68/100 of these, the % of YES responses will be between 66.8 and 73.2—i.e. within 3.2% of the true figure. With a question with higher variability, one in which 52% of respondents answer one way and 48% the other, the range increases to + 3.5%; and for a question of much lower variability, 90% answering "YES," the range narrows to + 2.1%.

3.10 *The main costs are incurred not in narrowing the range, but in increasing the probability of your sample estimate falling within that range.* The table gives figures for 68% probability, but to achieve the same range in a higher proportion of possible samples requires much larger samples. E.g. to get a range of +3.2% with 90% probability increases the sample size from 200 to 552. A further increase, to 95% requires a sample of nearly 800.

3.11 If these accuracy levels are disconcertingly low for the typical sizes of sample you can afford, you will need to consider more elaborate and accurate alternatives to simple random sampling, such as stratification, or even multi-stage designs combining a variety of sampling methods. In such cases the equations which relate sample size to accuracy are best left to professional statisticians.

Simpler ways of setting the sample size

3.12 If the complexity of these calculations deters many social researchers, so does the feeling that these statistical models barely mirror the hazards and unpredictabilities of real-world sampling. But there are some much simpler and more robust calculations which can give a rough idea of whether the sample will be sufficient for your needs. The most basic check is whether there will be enough people for you to reach some credible conclusions.

3.13 Say you were hoping that a Kings Fund survey would provide sufficient information to recommend improvements in hospital food. From previous surveys you know that around 87% of in-patients are satisfied with the quantity of food served. However, in this type of survey it is the patients' comments, not the absolute percentages, which lead to specific policy. From previous surveys you also know that around 15% are likely to make useful suggestions, so your sample of 200 will produce 30 usable comments. You assume that these 30 will be equally divided between those who have suggestions for reducing and increasing the amounts—and if it then transpires that each of these groups of comments can be further divided in three, there will be only 5 examples of each type of proposal—barely enough to form the basis for policy. You will need to increase the sample size; or alter the questionnaire so that it produces more relevant data.

3.14 Because most surveys not only want to present results for the entire sample, but are interested in the responses of specific sub-groups, or comparisons between sub-groups, you may have to do a similar calculation to estimate what proportion of your sample will belong to the groups in question.

3.15 Say you are hoping that a population survey will provide, amongst other things, useful information on the experience of retired respondents who have recently used chiropody services. Census data (albeit now 7 years old) will show what proportion of the local population are over retirement age—25%. If previous surveys suggest that approximately 60% of this group are likely to have had chiropody treatment in the past year, then for every 100 people interviewed, only 15 will fall into the requisite sub-group.

3.16 One can similarly predict whether there will be sufficient numbers in relevant groups to make intended comparisons. E.g. between those, over retirement age, who had private and NHS chiropody treatment. This particular comparison might need a very large sample.

§3.3 PRINCIPLES OF SAMPLING

3.17 The previous calculations and examples have been based on the principle of **simple random sampling**—i.e. of drawing individuals randomly from your entire population in such a way that every individual has an equal chance of being selected. But there are real practical difficulties with this method. It is the least accurate design; it can lead to geographically dispersed respondents and massive interviewer travel costs; and require very large samples if the views of particular groups are to be adequately represented.

3.18 Other approaches can overcome these difficulties and greatly increase the accuracy of estimate. The two most popular are **stratification** and **clustering**.

3.19 Stratification at first sight seems to violate the principle of randomness. It divides your target population into recognisable groups (strata)—samples randomly within each, *but at different levels*. Thus you can ensure that small but important groups will be sufficiently represented to be able to say something about their views.

3.20 The best-known application of this method is found in the way the UMIST/HPAU package uses different sampling fractions from wards with different patient throughput—i.e. it samples more intensively in wards with less patients, to ensure that all wards are represented in the final analysis. The overall sample will not be representative of the hospital, because some wards will be under- and others over-represented. But once results have been analysed by wards, figures for the entire hospital can be estimated by recombining weighted ward data.

3.21 In this way, stratification can be use to increase the representation of groups who might otherwise have to be excluded from any comparisons and analysis. Because of this, stratified sampling is nearly always more accurate than the simple random method. It also reduces costs and other difficulties in sampling from large populations. It is almost certainly bound to be a part of large multi-stage population samples.

3.22 In such a sample, stratification is likely to be linked to some form of **clustering.** The principle here is to choose a sub-group of the population which you think will be representative of the whole—e.g. researching selected villages in a rural area; certain districts in a town; or people only attending an out-patient clinic on certain days. Whereas stratification is premised on the notion of deliberately over-representing distinct groups, in clustering the sub-group or groups you choose must be, as near as possible, a microcosm of the whole.

§3.4 EXAMPLES

(i) When to do an A&E survey—an example of clustering and stratification combined.

3.23 A frequent problem, particularly in out-patient and A&E research, is deciding *when* to conduct a survey. Rather than simply nominating a week when researchers and helpers are available, you should attempt to devise a sample by something like the following process.

3.24 First, make some rough calculations of the number of respondents required to adequately report on the questions in your study. Then, from attendance statistics and discussions with staff, identify what constitutes a typical week or month and how this can be broken down into characteristic periods. Decide whether you want to stratify—i.e. over-represent some of these periods because they are the times when groups in which you are particularly interested attend. From response rates in previous studies, and known attendance levels, calculate how many periods of research are needed to achieve the desired sample.

3.25 All this is much easier to do than describe—and it has three distinct advantages over the blanket decision to sample for a solid one or two weeks. Firstly, it may save effort—sampling for an entire one or two weeks may produce an inefficiently large sample. Secondly, it permits the use of stratification to increase the proportion of groups in which you are particularly interested, but who only attend at certain times—a typical problem for A&E studies researching reasons for self-referral. Thirdly, even if you eventually decide that a concentrated period of research will be most efficient, having thought about alternative designs will have posed some useful questions about the sorts of data and issues involved.

(ii) A multi-stage population sample

3.26 Most moderate size surveys combine several different methods in a multi-stage sample. Consider a survey of a medium sized urban area .. Simple systematic sampling can be used for a postal survey (e.g. Maidstone 1987), but might yield relatively few replies from types of respondents and areas in which you are particularly interested. You might consider using stratification to increase their numbers. If you are planning to interview, or accompany the survey with focused local publicity etc.. you may well want to build some form of clustering into the design—i.e. concentrate on representative examples of particular types of area, rather than have to send interviewers around the entire town.

3.27 Using a sample of 2000 to cover a town of 100,000 might require:

1. Consider which major demographic factors, such as housing type and population age are most likely to influence the results.
2. From local area census data, planning reviews and other local knowledge, try to divide up the town into types of district distinguished by these factors. These will be your strata.
3. Decide what proportion of each type is to be included in the final sample (setting the sampling size for each strata).
4. Establish what proportion of the population lives in each;
5. Select areas which are to taken as representative of each type—i.e. use clustering to, e.g. choose which out of several inner city areas you choose. (perhaps 5–10 areas in all)
6. Set a sampling ratio for each area.
7. Propose a sampling method for each area (e.g. will there be further clustering concentrating on particular streets; will you work from lists of named individuals, or send researchers out to compile a list of households; what sort of replacement strategy..)
8. Draw the sample—either from a list; or by getting interviewers to sample every nth. household.

3.28 Your sample design points to a particular target group—what you now need are practical ways of finding that group and selecting representative members.

§3.5 SAMPLING FROM LISTS

3.29 Health authorities are unusually lucky in often having lists of names from which to sample. Other social researchers usually expend considerable effort having to compile ad hoc and not too satisfactory lists of suitable respondents. Or they may have to use "proxy" lists, when the individuals or units to be sampled are arranged in a quasi-list form—e.g. households arranged consecutively in a street, or patients in a ward. Once there is a well-defined list or proxy-list, the actual sampling is relatively simple and likely to be grounded in one of two methods: systematic and simple random sampling.

3.30 Systematic sampling means selecting every nth. name or household on the list, starting from a random point between 1 and n. This is the standard method.

Simple random sampling (SRS) vs Systematic Sampling

3.31 SRS is only to be preferred in 3 instances. The first two are when a systematic sample may introduce significant bias. Either when the sampling interval is a multiple of some recurring feature in the list; or if the list is arranged in, say ascending order of some relevant variable and the sampling interval is so large that the choice of starting point could produce an unreasonably small or large average value.

3.32 The usual objections to SRS are the effort in drawing samples, using random number tables etc., and the expense of sending interviewers to randomly chosen locations (especially in rural areas). When the latter is irrelevant, e.g. in a postal survey, SRS may be a cheap and efficient method if your name list is held on a computer database with the in-built capability of drawing random samples. This is the third instance in which it may have an advantage over the systematic alternative. Then there are only two considerations—do you really want an SRS when stratification etc. can be more accurate and can ensure higher numbers in strategic groups; and can your local statistician check that the pseudo-random number generation routine is being appropriately seeded and not always producing the same series of numbers.

3.33 Perhaps the most widespread error in using existing name lists is to assume they are something which they are not—of which the best known is the common illusion that the Register of Electors is a list of households, not individuals. This misconception has the following consequences. By sampling every nth. name from the list, you give each *person* an equal chance of being chosen, but each *household* has a chance proportional to the number of its members. If the subject of your survey is related to household size, as will be the case for most health surveys, then a sample of random individuals from the Register will be biased by over-representing the experiences of large households.

3.34 Such biases can usually be avoided—the most laborious method is to reorganise the Register of electors by household—difficult and uncertain with single addresses containing large groups of people with different second names. More simply, you can use "firstings" i.e. accepting names drawn systematically from the Register only if they are the first in a household (e.g.N.W.Durham 1986). If it also appears that your list systematically arranges members within households—i.e. tends to list the women before men, then you may want to choose a method in which you invoke two further randomising processes. First you identify the household by the usual systematic method; you then decide whether to sample from this household using a random process which has an average 1:n success rate, where n is the size of the chosen household. Having accepted this household, you will then want to add a further random choice to select one of its members, rather than automatically accepting the one given by the original list method.

Finding your target group—the plot thickens..

Lists and Proxy lists

3.35 Outside of the privileged sampling conditions of admission and discharge lists, you face much the same problems as other social researchers in trying to find usable lists of potential respondents. There are three approaches to achieving a sample of the general population—working from the Register of Electors; compiling a list, or proxy list, of households or apparently occupied addresses; or taking a quota sample of people in public spaces and other selected locations.

Sampling from the electoral register

3.36 Prior to anxieties that the Community Charge will lead to mass deregistration, the main drawbacks of the Register have been the relatively low number of registrations and the rapid population turnover in certain central urban areas. With more than 50% of the population changing address/ per year in some areas, and those same areas having large numbers who are not registered out of volition, apathy, landlords trying to prevent tenants registering etc., few serious researchers would use the Register as a sampling frame in such circumstances.

3.37 In the Spitalfields research (Tower Hamlets 1984), the Register was used as the starting point for compiling list of privately occupied addresses. It was corrected by a list compiled by a local housing study, and finalised after "Interviewers walked along all the streets in the study area noting all addresses which appeared occupied."(p.71)

3.38 In urban areas there will often be no alternative to compiling your own register, or letting interviewers treat apparently occupied addresses as a proxy list. You will undoubtedly encounter further difficulties—such as how to define a household and when to allow replacements, and might want the advice of people who regularly do this sort of survey. They may also be able to help with an additional problem—if you are sampling by households, do you accept the person answering the door as your respondent , or choose someone else. The normal circumstances in which you would want a different interviewee are: when your sample is of names from the Register and you have to contact a named person; when you ask the person answering for details of the household and then select a respondent randomly; or when you want to talk to someone with a particular role in the household.

§3.6 NO LISTS—NO STATISTICS—JUST *QUOTAS*

3.39 If lists are too slow, expensive and generally impractical for your purposes, you will need to adopt some sort of *quota sampling*. Beloved of market researchers, and usually applied to interviewing in public spaces, quota methods set each interviewer a daily target for the number and socio-economic characteristics of their respondents. In the simplest studies, quota are based on age and sex, E.g. an interviewer might be instructed to get replies from the following 50 people:

		F	M
Age	18–35	8	8
	36–60	7	9
	61+	10	8

3.40 Quotas will either be set to reflect the characteristics of the local population, or, as a form of stratification, to increase the contact with small groups of special interest. They can be adjusted during the study if certain groups are proving difficult to contact. Class and purchasing group are often added to age and sex in setting the quota. Questionnaires then have to start with screening questions to eliminate ineligible respondents. In the Salisbury study (88), the interview opened by asking about recent contacts with health services, then used different questionnaires for different groups of respondents.

3.41 Although the interviewers work to a quota, the sampling is still random, because everyone meeting the quota criteria has an equal chance of inclusion. For statisticians, the main drawback of quota methods is not really knowing the size of the target population. Just how many people walked through the town centre on the days of the survey? Since you do not know this number, you will not know the proportion sampled. You may be prepared to accept the statistical uncertainty—after all, not that many small health surveys actually calculate their accuracy levels—but can you be certain of finding a representative sample? Market researchers have the advantage that interviewing in shopping streets and precincts reaches precisely the sort of respondents they want, but you can be equally certain that the highest users of health services, the ill, the frail, the elderly, and mothers with young children, are least likely to appear in typical quota survey venues.

3.42 One alternative is to emulate public opinion surveys and conduct quota based house-to-house interviews. Interviewers call at every nth., address, until the quota is met. The more obvious biases are guarded against by interviewing at different times of day and on different days of the week, but there were no examples of this in the studies reviewed. Conscientiously done, it will be much more representative than public space interviewing, but proportionately more expensive. And the few health surveys which have the resources to interview large home based samples, seem to prefer the extra representativeness of list and proxy list methods.

3.43 Another useful modification is to target your research not at the whole population, but at groups frequenting particular places: hospital visitors, parents outside schools, clinic attenders etc..This may be the only practical way of reaching certain groups.

3.44 Even the cheaper and more common form of quota research, interviewing in public spaces, is rare in health research. Unless you can find unpaid volunteer interviewers, it will almost certainly be more expensive than a good postal survey with reminders, and will be far less representative.

Quota research is really only worth considering if you need a large number of responses quickly—e.g. when data is needed to respond to a sudden policy change, and/or if you know that your target population is easily found in a suitable public location.

§3.7 WAYS OF AVOIDING BIAS FROM NON-RESPONSES

3.45 Low response rates can destroy a survey—not just by reducing the amount of usable data, but by leaving the survey open to the charge of unrepresentativeness. The obvious solution is to do everything possible with the available resources to maximise response rates. In many cases, a small, high response survey is preferable to a larger, lower response exercise.

3.46 Maximising response rates must be subject to the usual caveats—the ethical objections of appearing to coerce your respondents, and the unreliable data that results. Interviews conducted on wards by hospital staff will be open to these objections.

3.47 *Replacement..* is a convenient way of increasing response rates, but it can bias your sample. In certain circumstances, replacement is legitimate—e.g. if you are trying to contact named respondents drawn from the Electoral register and their address is either missing or patently unoccupied—replacing them with their neighbours, or the next similarly sized household in the street is generally acceptable—but, for obvious reasons, calling at every address until you find someone in is not.

3.48 Once the data is collected you will almost certainly have suspicions that your method of collection has discriminated against certain groups, especially in postal surveys where response rates can be below 50%. Most texts on sampling describe the sort of groups, who are likely to be missed, e.g.: "as a result of the low response rate the sample is biased. It is no longer a random sample as intended but a sample of self-selected volunteers. These will usually be people who are interested, better educated, of higher socio-economic status, and, of course, those who have more leisure. Busy housewives with children will certainly be under-represented." (Gardner p.84)

§3.8 DETECTING BIAS

3.49 With an *interview based* study, your interviewers may be able to record quite detailed reasons why named respondents or those at given addresses are not available—address appears to be unoccupied ;demolished; new residents etc.. It is not unknown for interviewers to ask neighbours if they are likely to be able to contact respondents after several unsuccessful visits.

3.50 In *population surveys* you can check certain classification characteristics of your achieved sample with those of the known population. Whenever possible, checks are made on characteristics known to influence your data—but for practical reasons, these may be limited to age and gender, sometimes extended to housing tenure and social class.

3.51 A 1987 survey of Wolverhampton compared the age and gender make-up of its sample with the 1981 census data.

A Comparison with the 1981 census in Wolverhampton %

	Ages	Our sample	1981 census
Females	0–4	–	5.9
	5–15	–	16.6
	16–59	/1.1	55.9
	60–74	22.1	15.0
	75+	6.8	6.6
	All ages (numbers)	236	127,808

(Part of Table AII.1 – (Wolverhampton 1988))

3.52 Something similar can be done with *in- and out-patient surveys not based on name lists,* by comparing the sample's characteristics with aggregate patient records. At is simplest, this could check whether the proportions in the sample matched those in the wards and clinics covered.

3.53 A more precise comparison is possible when *samples are drawn from lists of patients*. Provided a record is kept of who replied, then you can make a detailed socio-medical comparison of your responding and non-responding groups. Finally, with a postal survey, you might consider dispatching interviewers to the non-respondents, or perhaps trying to contact them by phone; not necessarily with a view to collecting the original data, but trying to establish their general circumstances and reasons for non-response. Studies of after-care provision may arrange for this to become a routine part of the care effort.

§3.9 HONESTY—AND RESIDUAL DOUBTS

3.54 In one respect, all these checks can be positively unhelpful in confirming the unrepresentativeness of your sample. Whether you report this is a matter of conscience, but it should at least help build corrections into future surveys.

3.55 What, of course, you do not know, is whether the checks and controls have been adequate. Your respondents may match the population on what you believe are key variables, but may still be unrepresentative in areas vital to the research. Which only shows that sampling is as much about understanding the sorts of variables which could influence your data and thinking qualitatively about to avoid unrepresentativeness, as it is about calculating accuracy levels and precise sample sizes.

Summary
- Samples can be too large as well as too small
- Estimate if your sample will give sufficient replies to support firm policy recommendations
- Use stratification and clustering to reduce the overall size of the sample needed
- Whenever possible try to sample from lists—but make sure these are not a source of bias
- Low response rates can be fatal to a survey, so—try to maximise response rates, but beware of coercing respondents
- Test your sample's representativeness with some basic checks
- Try to get a sense of what will influence your data before designing the sample.

4. QUESTIONNAIRE DESIGN

This chapter discusses:

- whether you should design your own questionnaire
- the advantages of good presentation and layout
- different types of question and questionnaire layout
- different ways of asking the same question
- things to avoid, such as hypotheticals and leading questions

§4.1 INTRODUCTION

4.1 Good questionnaire design is probably the major factor controlling the relevance, reliability and validity of your data. Detailed help can be got from any number of texts,[1] though most concentrate on ways of avoiding disasters rather than guaranteeing success. The two most general rules are: keep length to a minimum; and do at least one pilot study.

4.2 However difficult, the temptation to keep adding questions should be firmly resisted. Data collection and analysis costs rise at least proportionately with questionnaire length. There are real dangers of becoming side-tracked and of the analysis and reporting being unfinished. If circumstances demand a general survey, then seriously consider one of the well-tested packages, but choose very carefully and critically from those on offer. They all collect rather different types of data and are therefore only capable of supporting certain types of conclusion.

4.3 Otherwise, make sure you only use questions which are directly relevant to your aims. Again, one cannot underestimate the importance of clear objectives. Long, unwieldy and confused questionnaires are easy enough to produce, and are that much easier if the survey as a whole has no clear sense of purpose.

4.4 Even if a questionnaire has previously proved successful in a similar study, it should usually be piloted in the specific circumstances of your survey. All new questionnaires should be piloted at least once and not just by friends and colleagues of the researchers. 30–50 responses should be sufficient for each pilot run and you may want to subsequently ask respondents, individually or in groups, what they thought of the questionnaire. If you are designing a self-completion questionnaire, you should also consider testing the wording by interviewing. Designing a self-completion attitude questionnaire will require a series of preliminary interviews and possibly a critical incident analysis to establish wording and topics relevant to your respondents—these can be expensive to develop.

4.5 Achieving excellence in wording and layout is of little use if the data cannot resolve your main questions. Check this by a manual analysis and dummy report on your pilot data. Does the questionnaire provide all the data needed for your report and are some questions patently redundant. Too many reports start with an exemplary statement of aims, but hedge the issues in the results section and cannot give clear conclusions because the crucial question was omitted, or the questions never quite got to the point. Analysing the pilot data could save the entire project from disaster.

§4.2 USING STANDARD QUESTIONNAIRES

4.6 In writing this chapter we considered including several examples of "good" questionnaires, or several composite questionnaires made up from examples of good questions. We eventually rejected this on several grounds.

4.7 It would have considerably increased the length of an already long document—to give a reasonable selection of questionnaires applicable to most consumer feedback situations would have needed a volume of its own. Choosing examples of good questionnaires would have not only been contentious but difficult. Not only is there no such thing as the perfect questionnaire, but questionnaires can be notoriously non-portable. One which has proved a great success in an adjoining Authority may, for reasons which are not always immediately obvious, be much less successful in yours.

4.8 Providing model questionnaires also contradicts much of our approach to design and analysis—that surveys should start with clear objectives and questions, and not just collect what is thought to be a standard range of data in the hope of something startling emerging. Having models to hand could discourage learning about questionnaire design, and there is a strong argument that before using someone else's questionnaire, one should be in a position to evaluate its merits and suitability for one's own precise needs.

4.9 We have tried to describe which sorts of questions and questionnaires are most suitable for different contexts in Booklet III, where we have also noted what topics have been successfully researched. Jones et al. (1985) is also a useful source of this information. We consistently found that the more precisely and narrowly defined a survey, the greater its chances of success. Using standard questionnaires may reduce the design effort, but it can increase the difficulties at all other stages. Rather than just reach for a standard model, we suggest that you:

- decide precisely what you want to find out, and whether a survey is the most appropriate method
- draw up a tentative list of questions, covering all the main topics you want to explore
- refer to previous studies. From what you know of question design, is their layout and wording of any questions an improvement on yours? Remember there may be advantages in using identical wording, as you could then have access to comparable data. At this stage you might decide that an existing questionnaire meets your needs sufficiently closely for it to be used in its entirety. If not, you must..
- design and compile the questionnaire.

§4.3 ASPECTS OF QUESTIONNAIRE DESIGN

4.10 The remainder of this section covers a number of rather standard points on questionnaire design. Most are applicable to both to self-completion questionnaires and interview schedules.

Presentation and layout
(Mainly for self-completion questionnaires)

4.11 Good design is not just a matter of aesthetic nicety but of directly improving the quantity and quality of responses. By modifying the cover and layout of her Kings Fund questionnaire, Raphael increased average response rate by over 10% and her original was by no means badly designed. With current pressures of time and money, densely packed and faintly xeroxed questionnaires are understandable, but they can damage a project.

33

4.12 At the very least, try to vary the typeface, and use good lining and headings. Will the local Area authority print unit provide free artwork, advice or letraset? Do any of the research team have graphics skills? Do CHC members have suitable contacts? Even experience of pasting up parish magazine/community papers etc. gives an idea of what is possible with limited resources. Using coloured paper may make the questionnaire more attractive and less official. On runs of several hundred or more, off-set printing is likely to be cheaper than xeroxing, permits the use of coloured inks and generally produces a more professional result. Ask the printers if they can do your cover-sheet artwork—this is unlikely to add much to the overall cost. Perhaps get an estimate from a Desk-top-publishing agency for doing your layout and art-work.

4.13 Remember you might need large print copies and/or translations, or questionnaires whose presentation and design is in some way dictated by your respondents.

4.14 When interview schedules and self-completion questionnaires are to be used for direct data entry, some part of the questionnaire will have to be used to carry code boxes. Adding these without destroying the legibility of your questionnaire is an art in itself. (See Fig. 4.1 for example).

Introductions and instructions

4.15 Questionnaires should begin with a clear friendly introduction setting out the aims of the project and asking for respondents help. The Kings Fund in-patient questionnaire can be taken as a good model, though some of its contents could be transferred to an accompanying introductory letter. The first page of a questionnaire often has some general instructions on how to answer the questions. Again try to keep these as short, simple and friendly as possible. If necessary, attach more specific and complex notes to individual questions.

The order of questions

(a) *Classification questions*

4.16 The only general rule is that personal classification questions: age,sex, occupation etc.. should be placed at the end and may need a separate introduction along the lines of:

> "In order to understand a little more about the people who are answering these questions, and in order to make sure that we have a wide spread of public opinion, we need to know a few personal details." (UMIST/HPAU)

and should contain guarantees of confidentiality. Avoid simply heading this section "personal details."

Help Us To Help You!

NORTH EAST ESSEX HEALTH AUTHORITY

We would be extremely grateful if you could let us know what you think of our outpatient facilities.

Please tick the relevant box and add any comments which may help us to improve the service.

| | For Office use only |

1. Which clinic did you attend? ....

2. How courteous/helpful were the staff?

| Very | | Fairly | | Offhand | | Unhelpful | | | |

Comments:

3. How long after your appointment time did you have to wait to see the doctor?

| Up to ¼ hr | | ½ hr | | 1 hr | | More than 1 hr | | | |

Comments:

4. Did you arrive early for your appointment?

| Yes | | No | | | |

5. How early did you arrive?

| Up to ¼ hr | | ½ hr | | 1 hr | | | |

Comments:

6. During your appointment was your illness/treatment explained to you?

| Fully | | Fairly well | | Poorly | | Not at all | | | |

Comments:

7. Did you understand the explanations given to you.

| Fully | | Fairly well | | Poorly | | Not at all | | | |

Comments:

Fig. 4.1

4.17 In certain cases these questions will have to be asked first—when interviewers have to pre-screen respondents.

(b) *Opening questions*

4.18 Interviewers appreciate opening questions which interest and involve the respondents so some sort of rapport can be quickly established. Questionnaires for self-completion may do better to start with quick, easy, but central questions to draw respondents in, and avoid any thoughts that their time is being wasted on trivia or irrelevances.

(c) *Filtering*

4.19 This refers to the process of directing different groups of respondents through different sets of questions, and should be avoided as far as possible in self-completion questionnaires. If two quite different sets of questions must be asked, why not use two questionnaires—though you then have two distinct data sets.

4.20 Other options are clearly labelling sections with headings such as: "to be completed by everyone; or please complete this only if..." and making these even clearer by printing sections in different colours.

4.21 If filters must be used, pilot them extensively and get them looked at by someone who enjoys logical puzzles. Errors can be costly and worrying. Your respondents will be faced with patently irrelevant questions and may give up altogether. Once a person has lost a filter route, they are unlikely to know where to re-start the questions. Filter errors may show up on data-entry checks, but then it is too late to know whether a respondent is answering inconsistently, or whether the questionnaire is at fault. If there is little data checking, filter errors will appear in the analysis when, for example, the number of a certain type of respondents as reported in one table, is different from those in another table supposedly only applying to those respondents. This seriously undermines the credibility of a report and is very difficult to correct once the data is collected.

Types of questions

(a) *Open questions:*

4.22 Examples of *open* questions are:

What did you like least about your stay in hospital?
What are your comments on the layout of the Department in the reception area?

4.23 With self-completion questionnaires, responses to open questions will either have to be subsequently coded (see chapter 7), or noted as comments to be used verbatim in reports.

4.24 Interviewers will either note answers verbatim, summarise them, or code them. Much of the overall coding work can be done in this way by interviewers though they will need to be well trained.

42. Did you go to any parentcraft classes?

GO TO Q44   YES (SPECIFY)................

                        NO ....

43. IF NO ASK "Why was that"

                NOT FIRST BABY ....

                DIDN'T KNOW ABOUT THEM ....

GO TO Q.45   TIMES OF CLASSES INCONVENIENT.......

                DIFFICULT JOURNEY ....

                DIDN'T THINK IT WOULD BE USEFUL .....

                OTHER (SPECIFY) ....

Example of filtering and interviewer coding

4.25 Rather than ask an open question and then code the reply into the boxes on the questionnaire, the interviewer may show a prompt card listing the options.

(b) *Closed & pre-coded questions*

4.26 In the prompted, open form, respondents use their own words which the interviewer codes. Closed questions such as the following, give no choice of wording.

Which of the following best describes your situation? (Tick one only)

I can get outdoors on my own with no great difficulty ❑

I can get outdoors on my own, but only with difficulty ❑

e.g. using stick, frame crutch or wheelchair ❑

I can get about in the house on my own, but I can

only get outdoors with someone's help ❑

I am chairbound ❑

I am bedridden ❑

(c) *Pre-coding*

4.27 Two of the main considerations in devising pre-coded questions are to make the wording and categories approximate your respondents views, and to generate data which will be comparable with other surveys and official sources.

4.28 Devising pre-coded attitude questions categories which approximate the patients views can be a lengthy and expensive process involving various combinations of observation, interviewing, critical incident analysis and extensive piloting. Not surprisingly, health authority surveys either tend to avoid such questions, or borrow from other studies. There are also moves to develop standard modules of questions which can be combined in different ways to construct individual questionnaires.[2]

4.29 The area where there is immediate room for improvement is for greater standardisation of the more factual questions. Taking 5 studies at random from the York archive revealed the following age scales.

0–16	under14	under 5	under25	under17
17–30	15–18	5–14	25–35	17–19
31–65	19–40	15–29	36–45	20–24
65+	41–60	30–44	46–55	25–29
	61–65	45–64	56–65	30 & over
	66–75	65 & over	66–75	
	75 & over		75 & over	

4.30 Different aims account for some of the variations in the lower categories, but the handling of the middle and upper age ranges is quite anarchic. The categories are so different that comparisons could not be made between the age data and age effects from these studies, nor in most cases with any official data.

Question layout

4.31 Questions which require a YES/NO response are favoured for self-completion because they are :simple to complete; easy to analyse; minimise ambiguity; and prompt respondents with standard lists of options. But critics argue that, especially with attitudinal questions, YES/NO formats can force stereotyped and over-simplified responses.

4.32 Here are 5 ways of asking about the information patients received.

1. Were you told enough about your illness and your treatment?

(Kings Fund)   YES/NO

2. Was the information you were given about your illness and your treatment

Much more than you had expected	❏
Rather more than expected	❏
About what you had expected	❏
Less than expected	❏
Much less than expected	❏

3. Were told enough about your illness and treatment?

Strongly agree	Agree	Disagree	Strongly disagree
❏	❏	❏	❏

4. Was the information you were given about your illness and treatment

Very helpful	Helpful	Adequate	Poor	Very poor
❏	❏	❏	❏	❏

5.

		Nurses	Doctors	Medical support staff
I always had to demand information about my treatment	from	❏	❏	❏
It was often necessary to ask for information about my treatment	from	❏	❏	❏
In order to receive information on my treatment I rarely had to request it	from	❏	❏	❏
Information on my treatment was always forthcoming	from	❏	❏	❏

(UMIST/HPAU)

4.33 *The different versions*

1. The wording of the first version is very vague—different respondents will interpret "enough" in different ways. It collects relatively little data—e.g. it doesn't ask how much information patients has received, only whether or not they thought it was enough. And it is relatively weak—with this

wording, most people (approx. 80%) will tend to say "YES." But to its advantage it is quick to complete and analyse and takes up minimal space on the questionnaire.

2. The second version provides a more sensitive measure, albeit at the cost of more space and slightly more analysis. Again, this is a question which asks not about the absolute information given, but the patient's perception of it. So there is the same problem as before—different people will have different expectations. And in this case, the wording is rather formal.

3. The third version seems an awkward alternative to the first two—while this type of layout has its uses, this particular wording is unsatisfactory.

4. The fourth is less formal than the third, but, again, there is some doubt as to what each point of the scale precisely means. It too is rather weakly worded and the majority of replies will be either "helpful" or "adequate."

5. The final version collects a great deal of information and tries to base its wording on the sorts of replies informants might give to an open question. Again, there are some difficulties with the wording—it is too formal, uses words such as "forthcoming" and the third option (an implicit double negative?) is quite hard to follow. The results might be unwieldy to present, unless summarised in index form.

4.34 Both versions 3 and 4 pose problems for analysis. With version 3, you may end up presenting the results as the number disagreeing vs. those agreeing—precisely equivalent to the "YES/NO" arrangement. Version 4 is not so easily simplified, and there remains the problem of how to present the results of a question to which the majority of people have given the median response. Both versions 4 and 5 can be summarised as indices, i.e. each point on the scale is numbered (usually 1,2,3,4,5) and the scores of a group of patients are added, and then expressed as a percentage of the possible maximum. Though easy to read, index values can be both ambiguous and confusing—chapter 8 describes some of the standard objections.

Things to avoid

(a) Hypotheticals

4.35 Data collected from hypothetical questions, such as

Would you be likely to use such a clinic

If so, about how often ....

is a routine part of most planning processes and is expected in making the case for new facilities. Except in very exceptional circumstances, the projections will far exceed initial use, but this will usually be allowed for and the viability of units should not judged by their ability to meet these projected targets..

(b) *Questions which tax the patients knowledge or memory*

4.36 Questions which cannot be answered because they tax the respondent's memory or are irrelevant to them. These will be over-general factual questions, such as asking about all previous visits to out-patient clinics; or questions which have slipped through the filtering logic. Both can confuse and demoralise. Even if the question is not patently irrelevant, you may be asking about subjects on which respondents are unlikely to have informed opinions. This may be glaringly apparent to interviewers, but hard to detect with self-completion forms.

(c) *Presuming questions*

4.37 That is, questions which make some presumptions about the respondents experiences. They are not necessarily bad but they will require you to use filters to ensure that questions relate to particular respondents experience. E.g. How long did you have to wait to see the doctor? is irrelevant to A&E patients who have only seen nurse/practitioners. Piloting should be used reduce the number of questions which make unwarranted assumptions about patients' experience—e.g. The Kings Fund question which assumes all patients are actually woken.

(d) *Leading questions and "learning effects"*

4.38 Leading questions, such as,

Do you find housework monotonous on the whole?

still occur in even the most prestigious of academic surveys and may be deliberately used to sensitise or politicise respondents. A widespread practice is to use surveys to inform about impending or possible changes in services. In its crudest form, it could mean a question such as:

Did you know that visiting hours are about to be reduced..?

4.39 A more widespread effect to which self-completion questionnaires are especially prone, is the problem of responses being biased by learning effects from other parts of the questionnaire. In extreme cases, questionnaires have been subdivided and parts distributed separately.

(e) *Ambiguities and double-barrelled questions*

4.40 The more obvious ambiguities—using terms such as "staff"—should be eliminated during piloting. More difficult are those cases where at the analysis stage a question seems likely to have meant different things to different

41

respondents. E.g. comparing smokers' and non-smokers' replies to: Would you be willing to accept smoking restricted to certain times and certain places ? is not comparing like with like, as this could well have had different meanings for the two groups. It is also a double-barrelled question and should be split into two.

(f) *Over-general wording*

4.41 Questions such as

Did the visiting arrangements suit you?

are unsatisfactory if what you really want is detailed feedback on signposting, car-parking, visiting hours etc.. Also try to avoid using vague qualifiers such as "generally."

(g) *Formal language*

4.42 Most questionnaires use over-formal language. Terms to avoid include: access; dissatisfied; resources; provision; consider; purchase; availability—all have informal substitutes.

4.43 The related argument is that formal language does not precisely express respondents' experiences—e.g. The UMIST questionnaire replaces the rather formal:

Was the choice and availability of newspapers

very satisfactory	❑
satisfactory	❑
unsatisfactory	❑
very unsatisfactory	❑

with a series of options including:

I never saw anyone bringing daily papers to the ward, which meant that we had to make our own arrangements	❑
By the time the papers were brought round to us, we were left with only a small selection to choose from	❑
We had a reasonable choice of papers and magazines most days	❑

the wording is still rather complicated but it is a useful attempt to bring typical experiences into the questionnaire.

SUMMARY

- Questionnaire design is probably the most important part of the survey, time spent here will pay dividends.

- However good the wording, a questionnaire which doesn't ask the right questions is useless. So good questionnaire design relies on knowing precisely what data you want.

- Only re-use another questionnaire if you are certain it collects the data you want.

- Questions and questionnaires should be as short as possible.

- Filtering should be kept to a minimum.

- Classification questions should be put at the end, unless needed for pre-screening.

- Questions should (amongst others):

  be unambiguous
  be informally worded
  not express opinions
  only convey a single idea.

Notes to Chapter 4

1. Most texts on survey methods have a section on questionnaire design. There are also many specialised works on psychological questionnaires.

   Payne, *The Art of Asking Questions*

   Moser and Kalton, *Survey Methods in Social Investigation*

   Oppenheim, *Questionnaire Design and Attitude Measurement*

   are some standard works.

2. Part of the Frenchay initiative proposes producing a series of re-combineable question modules. Both IIPAU and the CASPE team are also moving in this direction.

5. INTERVIEWING

This section covers:
- **When to use interviews—their merits and limitations**
- **Recruiting and training interviewers**
- **How many interviewers**
- **Do's and don'ts of interviewing**
- **Dilemmas**

§5.1 WHY INTERVIEW

5.1 Compared to self-completion questionnaires, interviews invariably collect fuller, more accurate data and are less likely to contain inconsistent responses . More sensitive topics can be covered, less demands are made on the interviewee and response rates are higher. And they can be used when self-completion questionnaires are inappropriate. Against this, interviews are costly, on time as well as money; and may inhibit interviewees' criticisms. A detailed summary of their respective merits and likely response rates can be found in French (1981), and a mass of useful advice and comment is given by Cartwright (1988), probably the most experienced user of interviewers in British health surveys.

When and where interviews are used

5.2 For obvious reasons of cost, interviewing has only been used in a minority of DHA and CHC surveys. Of the 166 more easily classifiable studies in major areas of the York archive, only 52 (32%) were interview based—mainly researching groups for whom the standard self-completion questionnaires are neither very relevant nor satisfactory.

	% studies done by interview
Elderly (15)	67%
Ethnic minorities (5)	60%
Accident & Emergency (9)	44%
Population surveys (22)	36%
In-patient surveys (35)	29%
Maternity studies (48)*	23%
Out-patient surveys (32)	19%
TOTAL N=166	32%

* some surveys in this group are with GPs & other health workers.

5.3 The types of interview, and who did them, varied enormously. In several studies, e.g. Waltham Forest (1986) and City & Hackney (1986), all interviews were conducted by the researchers, in both cases, students. Volunteers also played a large part, especially in CHC studies. Hospital staff were occasionally used, despite the potential problems of role conflict. MSC Community Programme and Job Creation Schemes have provided interviewers for some of the larger studies. e.g. Worthing (1977) and Sheffield (1978). In rare instances, such as Salisbury (1988), market research agencies conducted the research and used professional interviewers.

When is an interview not an interview..

5.4 Although, in principle, all interviewers should be carefully selected and trained to a high standard—in practice, who is used and how well they are trained is still likely to depend upon the type of study. There are three main settings:

1. Interviewing patients in wards, or in out-patient clinic waiting areas
2. Interviewing in the street or other public spaces
3. Interviewing respondents at home.

5.5 The line between offering to help with a self-completion questionnaire, and conducting a full-scale interview is both thin and blurred. Though it is crossed in many in- and out-patient surveys, few take the full implications on board—that if you plan to interview, then your questionnaire distributors should be appropriately trained; and if your self-completion schedule is to double as an interview schedule it should at least be designed for this dual role. Not only can the quality and quantity of data suffer, but both interviewers and interviewees can be put under stress. Interviewers should be trained to the point where they can make patients feel that their participation is genuinely voluntary and unrelated to their treatment and care. They should also be fully familiar with the questionnaire and what to do when their respondent in out-patient reception is not a patient but a patient's friend, or someone simply sheltering from the rain. Supervisors or other interviewers should be on hand to ensure that when questionnaire distributors have to conduct interviews, they can do so without having to keep checking on new arrivals and others who need questionnaires.

5.6 All these are obvious points, but easily overlooked, and hard to correct when the research is actually taking place.

5.7 The assumption that real interviewing starts with interviews on doorsteps and in the streets means that most studies using these types will pay some attention to interviewer training and recruitment.

§5.2 USING VOLUNTEERS

5.8 In a small study, researchers may decide to do the interviews themselves. This can have several advantages such as greater consistency in the way questions are asked and a greater likelihood of the recorded data meeting the needs of the questions. It can also have its drawbacks. The consequences of interviewer bias are that much more serious if only a few interviewers are used, especially so if those interviewers are researchers with strong preconceptions of what the results *should* be.

5.9 Volunteers should be used cautiously—they may be especially good at interviewing groups with whom they share experiences, but their effectiveness in general population studies is questionable. Experienced, well-trained interviewers get much higher response rates, at least 70–80%, volunteers only 50–60%. Volunteer response rates may even be lower than those in self-completion studies. Student volunteers, especially if used in large numbers, will require high levels of supervision; may not be highly motivated and, as a result, take less care in filling in schedules and be less inclined to follow up non-contacts. Volunteers may prefer interviews to be pre-arranged by post or phone, both likely to increase the refusal rate. Volunteers should also realise that they will normally need to be available for work at evening and weekends

§5.3 RECRUITING AND TRAINING

5.10 Quite different skills are needed for different types of interviewing and subject matter. Someone who is highly competent in building a relationship with a respondent in long sensitive interviews, may be quite unsuitable or unprepared for quota interviewing in a busy street. Recruiting interviewers gives you some control over who you use as workers, but at a price.

5.11 If you decide to employ interviewers, you, or your fieldwork supervisor, will have to:

- Advertise for applicants in the local press; or see if a local Polytechnic or University has a list of suitable names

- handle correspondence with prospective applicants

- interview applicants

- train them: likely to take at least 2–3 days and should include some field training

- insist on probationary period, so that unsatisfactory interviewers will not be employed on the main survey

- supervise and generally maintain contact with them during the research period and arrange regular de-briefings

§5.4 ORGANISING THE FIELDWORK

5.12 Other tasks for the interview supervisor will include:

- notifying local police of the survey, making sure it is entered in the station day-book

- prepare and issue interviewer identity cards

- arrange for a supply of questionnaires, covering letters, prompt/show cards etc.

- keep track of time spent/numbers of interviews done/ distance travelled by each interviewer

- make field checks.

§5.5 COSTS OF INTERVIEWING

5.13 Although some market research companies pay below this rate, most surveys will employ interviewers at between £3.50 and £6.00 per hour. Travelling and training time will probably be paid at a lower rate. Piece-rate schemes for long interviews with named respondents can pay as much as £10.00 – £15.00 per completed interview, but this will be expected to cover all travelling time. Piece-rates for short door-to-door interviews based on quota are likely to be between 60p. and £1 per interview.

5.14 Travelling costs will have to be met: 0.12 – 0.15p. per mile is usual. In urban areas it is safe to reckon that travel costs will be around 30% of interviewer salaries.

§5.6 HOW MANY INTERVIEWERS—HOW MANY INTERVIEWS

5.15 In all types of survey, but especially those done in respondents' homes, it is easy to underestimate the number of interviewers needed and fail to get the required number of interviews done in the allocated time. Allowing for their travelling time, finding specified addresses, refusals, up to 4 return visits at different times of the day and week, and the time and effort of conducting the interview, most interviewers should not be expected to complete more than 5 interviews in respondents' homes per day—though this might be doubled if interviews are very short, people are in, and the interviewer is able to call at every 2nd. or 3rd. door.

5.16 Far fewer should be expected, perhaps only 2 or 3 per day , if you have a specialised target population in scattered addresses and long and/or stressful interviews.

5.17 Quota interviewing in public places delivers far more respondents to the point where interviewer stamina can be the limiting factor. 30–50 interviews per day is not unreasonable with a short questionnaire, good weather and readily available respondents. However, rates can drop considerably towards the end of quotas, when people matching difficult criteria have to be found. Stories of interviewers cheating on their quotas and using inappropriate respondents can't all be untrue.

§5.7 THE INTERVIEW

5.18 Most standard texts on survey research list the main components of interviewer training and interview technique, but the manuals issued by survey organisations[1] are best for practical details. They cover the following sorts of points.

(i) Identity cards and friendly, informative introductions

5.19 Interviewers should always carry an identity card, which should be handed to respondents, not just shown.

5.20 In all but the briefest quota interviews, interviewers should fully explain the purpose of the survey and try to convince potential respondents of the value of the work. Cartwright (1988) explains that the Institute for Social Studies in Medical Care has a code of practice which requires interviewers to "say who they are, that is what organisation they come from, why the study is being done, how the person was chosen and what will be done with the information obtained."

5.21 Assurances about confidentiality should be convincing, as should any explanation of how the respondents name was obtained. Letters can also be left with respondents giving this information in more detail.

(ii) Repeat calls and doorstep "sifts"

5.22 The person answering the door may not always be your intended informant, so interviewers will have to arrange to return when they appropriate person is in. Interviewers may also have to do "doorstep sifts"—i.e. select a respondent from what the person on the doorstep tells you of the household, explaining that a certain household member is needed.

5.23 Repeat calls (a maximum of 4 is usual) will have to be made until the correct person is found. After 4 calls, the interviewer may need to operate some replacement strategy—e.g. call at the neighbouring household and repeat the doorstep sift.

(iii) Conducting structured interviews

5.24 Once the interview starts, the interviewer is responsible for asking the questions in the set order and using the precise wording on the questionnaire. Varying the wording can invalidate the responses, so the onus is on questionnaire designers to construct usable wording. Responses should be recorded as fully as possible, at the time, and in pencil.

5.25 In structured interviews, respondents should be kept, as far as possible, to the current question. Interviewers should record information which bears on later questions, but still ask these questions, with suitable apologies as necessary. Interviewers should be thoroughly familiar with the structure of filters in the questionnaire, so there is never any doubt whether a particular question should be asked.

5.26 Much of the skill in interviewing is in effectively probing for details without leading the respondents. Researchers should make sure that interviewers have a sufficient sense of the purpose of the work to understand what would be leading prompts. Probes should also be used when there seem to be inconsistencies in the replies.

5.27 In general, interviewers are required to do all they can to win the confidence and co-operation of their informants. But interviewers should not discuss their own experiences or opinions, or by their appearance and manner do anything which might bias the replies.

(iv) Coping with questions from your respondents

5.28 Having on the one hand to establish the necessary rapport to win the confidence of their respondents, while at the same time not expressing even the most general of opinions, presents a considerable dilemma for the interviewers and one which is heightened in several circumstances.

5.29 For example, in her series of 4 interviews with 55 women, twice in pregnancy and twice afterwards, Oakley (1980) was asked some 878 questions, including many requests for information—as she says "It would be the understatement of all time to say that I found it very difficult to avoid answering these questions as honestly and fully as I could" (p.43)

(v) Should interviewers offer help?

5.30 Interviewers may be valued as a social contact, as a source of information—in a number of ways which prejudice the very orthodox formal notion of a detached information gatherer. Interviewers may also feel an obligation to intervene when their respondent seems to be in need of social or medical help. Cartwright (1988) sets out the sorts of rules that would be agreed by most research organisations "In my view it is appropriate for the interviewer to advise the person where, or from whom, they might get help and to give them the names, addresses and telephone numbers. I think interviewers should offer to get in touch with the potential helper only at the informant's request, and should never do so without the informant's explicit agreement." (p183)

§5.8 DILEMMAS

5.31 These sort of dilemmas have led Oakley (1981) and others to argue that the traditional approach to interviewing is founded on a basic contradiction—between, on the one hand, establishing some sort of rapport, and on the other, trying to produce an interview which is bias free, structured and governed by different rules from ordinary social contact. These rules for interviewers are also criticised for being authoritarian and patronising at best. In this model, it is argued, there is a

50

fundamental power imbalance, between the interviewer who manages and manipulates the situation and the respondent who is expected to do no more than provide data.

5.32 Accepting these criticisms and taking the arguments on board, rules out the majority of surveys in the form they are presently conducted. They are not new objections. Since the development of public opinion polling in America in the 30's, some sociological and philosophical critics have argued against all surveys as phoney, bureaucratic and coercive forms of public feedback. Whether Oakley would go this far, given she herself is a survey researcher, is unclear.

5.33 What these debates have done, however, is to further alert researchers to the potential difficulties of the social dynamics of the interview. In most cross-sectional surveys, when interviewees are only seen once, and where the topics are not highly sensitive, interviewers are usually expected to follow the orthodox model—albeit with an awareness of the likely problems.

5.34 These rules are much harder to follow in the sorts of situations which Oakley describes—where informants are seen several times over a longish period; or where interviewer and interviewee are likely to have some shared experience bearing on the subject of the interview. In both these cases, but especially the latter, one should seriously consider using interviewers who are likely to be sympathetic to the informants by virtue of shared experience, and not attempt the traditional sort of interview which is likely to be strained. Doing this may have implications for the type of data which can be collected. You may have to accept that the situation is only likely to produce detailed qualitative data, more akin to critical incident analysis, rather than the standardised pre-coded replies of a more formal survey.

In summary

- **Compared to self-completion questionnaires, interviews:**

  collect fuller and more accurate information
  cover a wider range of topics
  get much higher response rates

- Interviews should almost always be used with certain groups such as ethnic minorities and the elderly

- **But interviews are expensive**

- **Finding and training suitable interviewers can be difficult and time consuming**

- **Avoid volunteer interviewers—except in highly controlled and supervised conditions. Volunteers can achieve even lower response rates than self-completion questionnaires.**

- Unless absolutely essential, don't pre-arrange interviews—it will reduce your response rates

- Interviewers should:

  give a friendly and informative introduction
  explain how the respondents were chosen
  stick precisely to the order and wording of the questionnaire
  be thoroughly familiar with any filtering
  know when, and how far, to probe for fuller replies
  not express their own opinions
  know what to do when respondents ask their advice or seem
  to need their help

- This standard interviewing model may need to be modified for those surveys where the interviewers repeatedly meets her respondents, or they have relevant experiences in common.

Notes
1. Such as that issued by the Office of Population Censuses and Surveys (McCrossan 1984); or by The Survey Research Centre at The University of Michigan (1970)

6. SHOULD YOU DO THE ANALYSIS? SHOULD IT BE COMPUTERISED?

§6.1 WHO DOES THE ANALYSIS—AND HOW IS IT DONE?

6.1 Grateful patients with home micros; MSC units; schools and higher education institutions; and commercial computer bureaux are just some of the people who have provided computer analyses for DHA and CHC surveys. Post Korner, and with the increasing power of office micros, most DHAs and their constituent units should now have access to computers suitable for survey analysis—either locally, or via a central services unit. But this need not necessarily mean they should be used to analyse your survey.

6.2 Even when there is ready access to a computer, you should ask if it runs suitable software, and if you know how to use it. If not, will you have to hand over the analysis to a distant unit which cannot meet your deadlines and can only provide an unintelligibly technical report? Should you do the analysis yourself and might you have been better off doing the analysis by hand?

6.3 At an early stage in planning the survey, you must decide whether you are going to:

- **pass the questionnaires to a separate unit for analysis and, possibly, reporting;**
- **code and check the data yourselves, enter it on to a computer, and then pass on the computer data file for analysis;**
- **do the analysis yourselves by hand;**
- **do the analysis yourselves, by computer.**

6.4 Should you do your own analysis?

(i) If you have the time, with a small survey it is worth doing the analysis yourself, by hand.

(ii) If the volume of data is such that the analysis needs to be computerised, are you then able, and do you want to do the analysis yourself?

§6.2 DOING THE ANALYSIS BY HAND

6.5 When is it feasible?

There are no immutable rules, but typically, when:

- there are less than 100 responses (though in one case, a CHC managed to analyse 500 Kings Fund questionnaires quicker by hand than by computer) AND

- the questionnaires are short and pre-coded AND

- you only need 1-way frequency counts and the occasional tabular comparison

6.6 When is it preferable?

- if you have a small (under 30–50) number of long questionnaires (setting up the computer analysis will offset any time savings)

6.7 When it may be preferable

With a sample of between 30 & 100 questionnaires, if you only want simple frequency counts, whether or not to use a computer should depend on the following:

- have you used computers before?

- will you have to learn how to use the analysis package?

- is there any clerical/typing support for data preparation and entry?

- will the analysis have to go to another department (the time spent on liaison may actually exceed the time it would take you to do the analysis by hand)?

- do you need the results very quickly?

6.8 When to combine manual and computerised analysis

Any parts of the questionnaire containing open-ended comments which you want to summarise without coding will have to be analysed by hand. It is quite common to find surveys using computers for their pre-coded and more easily coded questions and analysing a few of the more expansive open questions, and all comments, by hand.

§6.3 SHOULD THE ANALYSIS BE COMPUTERISED?

6.9 The advantages of computer analysis are well-known:

- it can handle much larger data sets (though beware of the temptation to produce over-long questionnaires and over-large samples)

- it should be quicker (especially if you need anything more than a few basic frequency counts)—it drastically reduces the amount of tedious and routine tasks for the researchers (though it creates almost as much, even more boring, work for clerical assistants and keyboard operators)

- it generates tabular and graphical output for printing or importing into word-processed reports—with the more specialised survey analysis packages, rather than a standard office database:

- it performs types of correlational analysis which would be prohibitively time-consuming if done by hand

- it allows a great deal of flexibility in the analysis; you can explore possible correlations and differently constructed indices.

6.10 You will undoubtedly hear stories of large surveys done miraculously quickly by computerisation—these are not necessarily apocryphal. But for each of these, there are many reports of studies abandoned, or hopelessly delayed, of partially completed reports or analyses having to be removed from the computer and finished by hand..

6.11 Basically if you have any doubts about your competence, or computer access, then analyse small to medium surveys by hand or get them done by a unit with a good record of producing competent reports on time.

§6.4 WHAT YOU NEED TO DO YOUR OWN COMPUTER ANALYSIS

6.12 The requirements are:

- **Considerable keyboard operator or word-processing/secretarial time**
- **Expertise in running a suitable analysis package and very basic statistics**
- **Suitable computing facilities which tend to be of two types:**
  1. Office databases with statistical summary and graphics options
  2. Purpose built survey analysis packages (such as SPSS)

Both can be run on office micro's, but survey packages are more likely to be found on mini's and mainframes.

6.13 Do not assume that any office data base will be suitable. DbaseIII, for example, is not and needs additional graphs and statistical utilities. You might need expert advice on whether your local database and micro are suitable.

§6.5 DATA ENTRY VS. DATA ANALYSIS

6.14 Remember that the computer being used for the analysis does not also have to be used for data entry. Most office word-processors are perfectly suitable for entering survey data—and you have the advantage of typists who are very familiar with these systems. Once a data file has been created by a word-processor, it can easily be transferred to the final analysis machine. Transfer will usually be by floppy disc or serial communications line.

Should you get someone else to do the computer analysis?

6.15 Your regional or district computer unit, or a university department, may be prepared to take your questionnaires and provide a statistical report. There are three main objections—they may not meet your deadlines; they do not fully understand the issues and your interests; and you tend to lose touch with the data. The last two factors should not be underestimated. With your detailed knowledge of the aims and objectives of the project, and the conditions being researched, you will continually find yourself asking new questions of the data during the analysis and be immediately able to put the answers into context. Very few outside analysts and reporters will be capable of this. In much social research it is an unwritten rule that for precisely these reasons, you do not give up your data to outside analysts and statisticians.

6.16 If you are unable to do your own analysis, think very seriously whether you need the survey in the first place. .If you do, ensure that whoever will be doing the analysis is an integral part of the team from the start.

6.17 Finally, most of these comments have been directed at units doing the occasional survey. Quality assurance offices, or any other group which is likely to do repeated survey work should consider investing in suitable computing facilities—probably software to run on existing machines; and ensure that at least two members of staff are thoroughly trained in its use.

7. DATA PREPARATION AND CODING

§7.1 THE OVERALL PROCESS

7.1 This section covers the laborious but important stages between collecting the data and starting the analysis. These are illustrated in the diagram on the following page.

7.2 Unless you have chosen to send your questionnaires, unchecked, to another unit for analysis, you are now going to have to be prepared to do some of the following as the data arrives.

§7.2 COLLECTING AND CHECKING THE DATA

7.3 As questionnaires arrive, they should be numbered, dated and checked for obvious errors. Any significant comments and complaints should be noted. This should be done as soon as possible to identify any difficulties with the questionnaires or with the interviewers. Various other tasks will need to be done at this stage as appropriate. These are likely to include: checking off the names of respondents; sending out reminders; debriefing interviewers; adjusting quotas; distributing more questionnaires.

7.4 Information may now be collected which could be useful to future surveys. In a self-completion study this could involve noting how rapidly questionnaires are returned, when return rates dwindle, and the effectiveness of reminders. In an interview survey, call-back, non-contact and response rates should be compiled for individual streets.

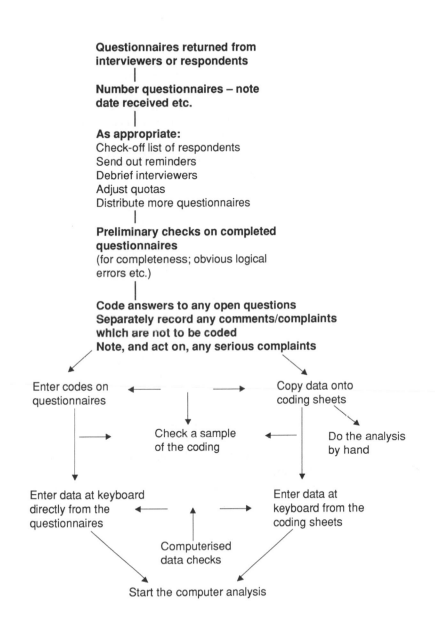

Questionnaires returned from
interviewers or respondents

Number questionnaires – note
date received etc.

As appropriate:
Check-off list of respondents
Send out reminders
Debrief interviewers
Adjust quotas
Distribute more questionnaires

Preliminary checks on completed
questionnaires
(for completeness; obvious logical
errors etc.)

Code answers to any open questions
Separately record any comments/complaints
which are not to be coded
Note, and act on, any serious complaints

Enter codes on
questionnaires

Copy data onto
coding sheets

Check a sample
of the coding

Do the analysis
by hand

Enter data at keyboard
directly from the
questionnaires

Enter data at
keyboard from the
coding sheets

Computerised
data checks

Start the computer analysis

§7.3 PREPARING THE DATA FOR ANALYSIS

(i) Coding

7.5 Coding is the process of converting your respondents' replies into standard, easily handled categories. Often overlooked as uninteresting and unproblemmatic, it holds sufficient dangers to be taken more seriously. And in most surveys, it is the one stage, apart from the data gathering itself, at which errors can enter. Coding can be done after the data is collected, or, as in most health surveys, at an early stage and built into pre-coded questions.

7.6 Most questions in consumer feedback surveys are PRE-CODED—i.e. either the respondent or the interviewer ticks (or otherwise marks) a box on the questionnaire.

1. Which of the following would you like to see in this hospital? (please tick just one)

   No smoking at all ❑

   Specially allocated smoking areas ❑

   No restriction on smoking ❑

2. Do you have use of a car   YES ❑   NO ❑

Two pre-coded questions

7.7 With pre-coded questions, the onus is on the questionnaire designer to do preliminary research and pilot work to ensure their categories faithfully reflect the respondents' perceptions. Once a self-completion questionnaire is in regular use, it can be very hard to identify and correct errors. They may show-up in an abnormally high level of "OTHER" responses, or in a general instability in the pattern of replies, but are otherwise hard to identify, short of directly asking respondents what they thought of each question—which most researchers are unfortunately reluctant to do.

7.8 With open or uncoded questions, respondents are allowed to give their replies verbatim e.g.:

What do you think was the best aspect of your care?

_____

An open question

(ii) Coding open replies

7.9 There are 2 main situations in which you will be coding open responses—when you want to apply a standard coding scheme, such as the Registrar General's Classification of Occupations; and when you what to provide a coded summary of uncoded data such as patients' comments or replies to a question such as:

What did you like best about your stay in hospital ....

This particular question has been used so often that you could adopt a coding scheme from previous studies. The categories nurses/staff/doctors/other-patients/rest and relaxation should cover the majority of replies.

7.10 To devise your own scheme, you should draw a random sub-sample of between 50 and 100 questionnaires-the number needed will depend on the range of replies; and develop the categories by summarising the responses. A question covering aspects of hospital experience should be straightforward, coding opinions is less so. You may need to copy your sub-sample of replies on to index cards and try sorting them into different sets of categories. Extra codes can always be added later, though this can get out of hand.

(iii) Using a standard coding scheme

7.11 There are several standard coding schemes which you may find useful. Each comes with some sort of technical manual and guarantees compatibility with at least some other surveys. The Registrar General's classification is one such, and is used in many academic and some DHA surveys. It converts the respondent's description of their occupation into 2 codes: one on an ordered 6 point scale based on occupational skill (The Social Class scale):

I Professional, etc. occupations
II Intermediate occupations
III Skilled occupations
    (N) non-manual
    (M) manual
IV Partly skilled occupations
V Unskilled

and another on a non-ordered 17 category classification which "aims to bring together people with jobs of similar social and economic status." These 17 categories (there are 3 additional sub-categories) include:

1.   Employers and managers in central and local government, industry,commerce etc.—large establishments
1.1 Employers in industry, commerce etc..
1.2 Managers in central and local government, industry commerce etc..
6.   Junior non-manual workers including non-supervisory clerical and sales workers
7.   Personal service workers
14. Own account farmers
16. Members of armed forces

7.12 The classification handbook gives the relevant codes for around 25000 named occupations, provided the description given by the respondent is detailed enough. "Engineer" is an oft quoted example of an inadequate description, but a frequent problem arises from researchers failing to realise that a number of the S.E.G. codes depend on the size of the establishment at which the person works—data which is rarely collected. A not uncommon scene in coding rooms is of coders and supervisors trying to guess this information from what they know of the local industry, from their estimates of the respondents' incomes etc..

(iv) Codebooks

7.13 All but the most pre-coded of surveys will produce some sort of codebook as a permanent record of the codes in use, and as a manual for the people actually doing the coding. This codebook will list each question, how it is coded, into which column the data should go on the data grid, and where to record information such as questionnaire number.

Use code "0" throughout for missing data Use code "9" throughout for missing non-applicable questions			
Question number	Column number	Question	Codes
	1-3	Questionnaire no.	
1	4	Clinic attended	Medical 1 Surgical 2 Orthopaedic 3 Dermatology 4 Gynaecology 5 E.N.T. 6
2	5	Staff courtesy	Very 1 Fairly 2 Offhand 3 Unhelpful 4
3	6-8	Waiting time	(Minutes)

Extract from a codebook

§7.4 CODING SHEETS AND DATA ENTRY

7.14 Coding will either be done on the questionnaires themselves, and the data typed directly on to a keyboard. Or coding will be done as all the data is transferred to coding sheets. Coding sheets are suitable for both manual analysis and for use by keyboard operators.

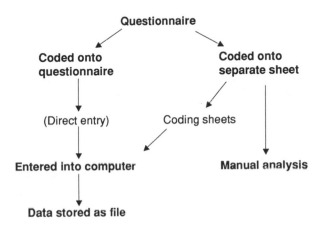

(i) Coding sheets for manual analysis

7.15 Although some small simple surveys are still analysed by counting directly from the questionnaires, the usual practice is to copy the data, coding as necessary, on to coding sheets. The reliability of this process can be dramatically improved by marking of the columns of the sheet with headings showing what data should go where.

7.16 THE DATA will then be in the form of a grid with the following characteristics:

- each row contains all the information from a single questionnaire;

- all rows contain the same number of items in the same order and are exactly the same length.

- all entries are numeric (though most analysis packages will handle alphanumeric data, this is generally inadvisable);

63

- all rows start with a question number or similar identifier (not to violate respondent confidentiality, but to enable the coded data to be checked against the original questionnaires)

- each column, or set of columns, containing a single piece of information is known as a variable.

(Table 2—Chapter 8 is an example of a data-grid)

§7.5 ENTERING THE DATA ON A COMPUTER

(i) Coding sheets vs. direct entry

7.17 With computerised analysis, you will have to decide whether to use coding sheets, or whether to type directly from the questionnaires.

(ii) Direct entry

7.18 Direct entry questionnaires are widely used in market research and the practice has spread to a number of health authority surveys. They can usually be recognised by the "for office use only" column giving the numbers of the columns into which the data has to be typed. Not having to prepare coding sheets can be a considerable saving, but direct entry has its own disadvantages.

7.19 They need more keyboard operator and keyboard time. There is a higher likelihood of entry errors, as even the best organised questionnaires are harder to read than coding sheets. Data error can be reduced by form-style entry, but this further slows the process and involves extra set-up time. Direct entry rarely eliminates the coding stage; all but the most heavily pre-coded questionnaires will require some preliminary work.

7.20 In general, direct entry is best limited to occasions when keyboard operator and computer access time is not at a premium. When keyboard operators are part of the research team and can identify any difficulties with individual questionnaires and resolve any coding problems. When questionnaires are short (preferably single sheets), extensively pre-coded and designed with the interests of the typist as well as the respondents in mind.

(iii) Form entry vs. data grids

7.21 Whether typing from coding sheets or from the questionnaires, there are two standard ways in which data can be put onto a computer.

(iv) Form entry with database packages

7.22 The first is via a data-entry screen, which prompts for each piece of information in turn and may do a number of range and type checks during data entry. Screens can be constructed with most database systems and some survey packages. They should cut down data entry errors, especially if working directly from questionnaires, but they may take several hours to set up and considerably reduce the speed at which data can be entered. Once in the computer, the data will usually be held in grid form.

(v) Using a word-processor to enter the data

7.23 The faster, but more error prone alternative, is to type in the data as a block of numbers, using any standard office word-processor set to its edit, rather that word-processing mode. Nowadays, almost any micro can be used for data input, with the advantage of using a word-processor which is familiar to research and secretarial staff. Data can be transferred to the analysis machine either by compatible floppies, or by one of the standard transfer programmes, such as Kermit.

§7.6 HOW LONG WILL IT TAKE?

Time to allow for checking and coding

7.24 Questionnaires should be checked for incompleteness, invalid responses etc., by a small group of trained checker/coders. Allow around 15–20 minutes per 15 page questionnaire for coding, numbering, editing, noting comments and general tidying-up, much less, say 2–3 minutes, if the questionnaire is short and heavily pre-coded.

7.25 A Kings Fund questionnaire might take an average of 3 minutes. So allow at least 20 person hours for 400 questionnaires.

Time needed for data entry

7.26 Questionnaires have a habit of generating large quantities of data. There may be only 50 questions, but if many are multi-part, and, if more than one reply is allowed, each option in a multi-choice question may have to be treated as a separate question. To estimate how long it will take to type in your data, you need to know how many numeric codes will be produced by a single questionnaire.

7.27 For example, the 1969 version of the Kings Fund standard in-patient questionnaire contains 37 questions—mostly single part. The pre-coded questions generate 42 numbers. Add a further 6 for the coded replies to the 3 open questions; and 12 to record the hospital, ward, date and other clerical information, such as questionnaire number—you now have 60 in all. So a study with 400 replies and this relatively short and simple questionnaire would generate 24,000 numbers!

7.28 A longer questionnaire with 50 or more questions, covering say 8–10 pages of A4 could easily produce a string of coded data 400 numbers long especially if some of the questions are multiple choice or multi-part.

7.29 With very well designed questionnaires, and keyboard operators familiar with their particular questionnaires, OPCS reckons that "in order to be regarded as proficient, operators are expected to key at the average rate of 72,500 key depressions per day."[1] That corresponds to just over two 80 character lines of information per minute—a very high rate working from direct entry questionnaires.

7.30 A good typist on a familiar word-processing system ought to be able to approach this speed when working from coding sheets, but better to allow much longer, say one minute or more per line and also allow for regular breaks. For direct entry, 2 minutes per 80 character line would be safer. At this rate, the 400 response Kings Fund example would take 10 hours of keyboard time.

7.31 Typists and clerical staff may be understandably unwilling to take on long stretches of this type of immensely mindless, but arduous work; and you may not have this level of access to keyboards in the research period. If your data entry time is so limited, you should consider employing sufficient coder/editors to provide the data-entry typists with coding sheets. Or, contract out the input. Many domestic and personal word-processors are also suitable, but beware compatibility problems with the Amstrad WP series.[2]

§7.7 WHAT CAN GO WRONG?

(i) Coding and data entry errors

7.32 The only certainty regarding coding and data entry is that it will be more error prone than you could possibly imagine. And that the resulting errors will be difficult to both detect and correct. Even if error rates are numerically insignificant, 5% or less, they will be surprisingly visible when you have to eliminate erroneous responses from every variable and each piece of data presentation is based on a different total.

7.33 Errors can enter at almost any point in the coding and data entry, but they will basically be of two types, the insidious and, hopefully, relatively low level of errors in copying, numbering and keyboard entry; and the much more spectacular problems associated with coding open-ended responses.

(ii) Copying and entry errors

7.34 Even the most routine aspects of data handling can be surprisingly error prone. Copying pre-coded data from a questionnaire onto a coding sheet, or converting pre-coded responses into numerical codes, can involve error rates of between 5 and 10%. Checking for such errors is notoriously difficult. Packages with form-style entry options, usually perform some sort of rudimentary type and range checks, but these will fail to trap the most common errors, copying, writing or typing the wrong, but in-range number. More specialised survey packages allow you to include more sophisticated multi-variable checks, but these are time consuming to devise and are likely to catch only the more bizarre combinations—10 year old grandparents etc.. Unless you can identify a particularly problematic part of the questionnaire in which the errors are concentrated, the only effective check for low level scattered errors is to entirely re-process the data and check any discrepancies. This may seem excessive, but in small to medium surveys it could be quicker than having to correct individual errors as they show up in the analysis.

7.35 In any event, you should re-enter a small randomly selected sample of the data both early on and at the end to: (a) check for systematic mistakes in the data handling and (b) estimate the level of coding/entry errors prior to deciding if more extensive checking is needed. If possible, do this by asking a separate coder and typist to re-enter a sample of your data, and compare it with the original. With clinical data, a very high level of accuracy would be needed, but most social surveys are content with an error level of 2–5%. If randomly occurring errors are higher than this, try to supervise the data coding and entry more closely. If systematic errors are found, identify and correct their cause and modify any other erroneous data.

7.36 If coding sheets are used, it is also worth making a quick visual comparison between them and a data print-out.

7.37 As even dedicated researchers are prone to the potential boredom and pressures of long-term coding, the obvious preventative measures are to be found in good questionnaire and coding sheet design and a sensible working environment and work rate.

(iii) Errors when coding open questions

7.38 The most significant errors occur in the coding of open questions—either with self-devised or official coding schemes. Often these are not strictly *errors,* but are differences of judgement when coders have had to fill in missing information, either because the respondents have been unforthcoming or the questionnaire has failed to prompt for full details. In such circumstances, coders may, amongst others:

- guess a code from other data on the questionnaire (i.e. assume the responses conform to some pattern)
- use the most common, or most general code
- choose a code at random
- use the code for "no data/no response" (sometimes the code for not applicable which causes havoc in filter checks)
- ask a supervisor, who may well do any of the above..

7.39 Recoding a random sample of questionnaires is the standard method of estimating the reliability of the coding. Even with well designed and heavily tested schemes, 40% differences are quite common and 70% not unknown—i.e. in only as few as 1 in 4 cases do two coders give the same code. Measures to improve the reliability of coding open responses include:

- if nothing else is done, pilot the questionnaire and coding scheme to ensure that sufficient information is gathered and that categories are comprehensive and mutually exclusive
- provide adequate coder training and supervision
- get coders and supervisors to systematically record any difficulties and the questionnaires/questions where these arose; periodically review the rules for recoding the more problematic questions and be prepared to entirely recode these if necessary
- allow sufficient time for coding
- avoid paying coders on piece-rates

§7.8 ALTERNATIVE METHODS OF DATA ENTRY

7.40 There are now mechanical ways of eliminating much of the work of data preparation and entry.

(i) Machine readable questionnaires

7.41 There are still in their infancy and extremely rare in health surveys. The simplest type of machine readable questionnaire uses white patches within dark squares instead of the usual YES/NO options boxes. Respondents select options by obliterating the white patches. More sophisticated optical scanners allow more conventional questionnaires, but cost considerably more and their use is limited to the larger market research agencies on large routine surveys.

7.42 The CASPE project at Bloomsbury reports reasonable success with the simpler type, but even this involves hardware and installation costs which outweigh any savings unless many thousands of standard questionnaires are to be used and speed is crucial. There is the further drawback that all machine readable systems are restricted to pre-coded data, and if one wants to incorporate respondents comments, these will have to be read separately and coded manually, defeating most of the advantages of the mechanical approach. (Part of the CASPE machine readable questionnaire is reproduced in section §2.4)

(ii) Computerised questionnaires

7.43 Showing the questions on a computer screen and getting respondents, or interviewers to type in the answers eliminates almost all separate data preparation and entry work. When done by interviewers, it can make for good interview dynamics—as the respondent and interviewer work jointly through the questions. Respondents seem to enjoy the experience as they can both read the questions and see their answers recorded.

7.44 As far as we know, the only example of this method being used in a British health survey is the study being run by Sheila Jefferson for Northallerton DHA, in which interviewers take respondents through 16 or so pre-coded questions. The success of the pilot work suggests this method deserves further attention, perhaps being extended to respondent direct entry. The relatively cheap and simple technology involved—DbaseIII programmed screens on an IBM PC—is competitive with the costs of staffing an orthodox survey. The system has potential advantages over machine readable questionnaires, and American experiments give an idea of how far one can go towards getting respondents to enter uncoded comments at a keyboard.

In summary

- **Decide in advance whether you intend to use coding sheets or direct entry from questionnaires**
- **Make sure you allow sufficient time for data checking and entry**
- **Number and check questionnaires for errors as soon as they are returned—scan any comments for major issues and complaints**
- **Decide whether to code all your data, or leave some of the more open comments for manual summary**

69

- Try to use standard coding schemes whenever possible

- Consider using your office word-processor for data entry

- Set sensible work rates for both coders and keyboard operators—overlong sessions and excessive rates can spectacularly increase the errors

- Check for systematic errors at every stage of the coding and data entry.

Notes

1. L. McCrossan (1985) *A Handbook for Interviewers*, p.90.

2. The Amstrad WP series uses 3 inch (not 3.5 inch) floppy discs which are physically incompatible with most other machines. Adding a serial communications port is an expensive option, and the earlier versions of the bundled software will not generate flat ASCI files. In all, transferring data from an Amstrad WP (though not the Amstrad PC series) is at best a difficult or relatively expensive business.

8. ANALYSING THE DATA

This chapter includes:

- some general encouragements for people wanting to do their own analyses
- ways of computing and presenting one-way frequency counts
- methods for summarising replies to numerical and scaled questions
- cautionary advice on indices
- simple ways of exploring correlations using crosstabulations
- statistical tests suitable for contingency tables
- notes on the main stages in a computer analysis

§8.1 NOT SO MYSTERIOUS

8.1 The general atmosphere of mystery and fear surrounding statistics has long been a deterrent to people doing their own analysis. A great pity, since the ability to count and calculate percentages is all the statistical ability one needs to analyse most social surveys.

Too much analysis

8.2 Such anxieties are often grounded in a model of analysis as something technical and impenetrable which is done to the data after collection.

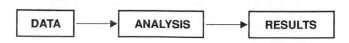

8.3 This picture of captive data, waiting for analysis, quickly leads on to the notion that the more analysis, and the more sophisticated the techniques, the better the results. By and large this is nonsense. It completely overlooks the purposes of the survey—that you collect the data to answer specific questions, not to test out different analysis techniques.

8.4 Whether or not the data is capable of providing the answers is another matter. This should have been checked by a trial analysis during the pilot phase.

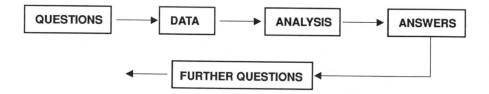

§8.2 ASKING THE QUESTIONS—DOING THE ANALYSIS

8.5 Most of the following examples are based on a fictitious sample of 365 out patients answering the questions in Table 1. These questions were chosen only to illustrate different types of analyses and very definitely not as examples of good design. Table 2 shows the coded data from 20 respondents replies to these questions.

Table 1 A Dummy questionnaire

Interviewer to code

(8.34–8.35, 8.42–8.44)
(8.7)

Questionnaire number ———
Clinic attended (code 1–8) ———
Waiting area   (code A–E) ———
Gender (F/M) ———

1. How did you travel to the clinic today? (tick one)

Car   Bus   Hospital car   Ambulance   Other   (8.6–8.8)

❏   ❏   ❏   ❏   ❏

2. Which of the following do you think best describes the out-patients department?
   (as many as you wish)

Welcoming   ❏

Comfortable   ❏

Pleasant   ❏

Efficient   ❏

Clinical   ❏

Disorganised   ❏

Confusing   ❏

Frustrating   ❏

Like a railway station ❏   (8.15–8.17)

Other (specify)   ❏

3. Thinking about the Health Service in Thursby, do you feel that the
   service offered is:

Very good   Good   Average   Poor   Very poor

❏   ❏   ❏   ❏   ❏
                                                        (8.18–8.20)

4. How long did you have to wait after giving your name to Reception
   before seeing a doctor or nurse?   (minutes)

————————————   (8.27–8.29, 8.37)

5. When you arrived, how long did you think you would have to wait?

No idea ❑

Less than 5 minutes ❑

6–10 minutes ❑

11–15 minutes ❑

16–20 minutes ❑

21–45 minutes ❑

46 and over ❑

(8.30)

6. How long was it before you were actually seen?

1–12 minutes ❑

13–22 minutes ❑

23–37 minutes ❑

38–50 minutes ❑

51 and over ❑

(8.31)

7. Did you feel that the temperature in the waiting area was:

Too hot   Comfortable   Too cold

❑   ❑   ❑

(8.34–8.35, 8.42–8.44)

8. Which of the following best describes you feelings about the medical care and general attention you received.

Very satisfied   Quite satisfied   Not satisfied

❑   ❑   ❑

(8.36, 8.37–8.39)

Examples of how to analyse these questions can be found at the paragraph numbers given in parenthesis

Questionnaire number			Clinic	Waiting area	Gender	Travel (Q1)	Q.2 Welcoming	Comfortable	Pleasant	Efficient	Clinical	Disorganised	Confusing	Frustrating	Railway station	Other	Health Services (Q.3)	Waiting time (Q.4)		Expected time (Q.5)	Wait time (Q.6)	Temerature (Q.7)	Care .. (Q.8)
1	2	3	4	5	6	7	8	9	10	11	12	13	14	15	16	17	18	19	20	21	22	23	24
0	0	1	2	1	2	5	0	1	1	0	0	0	0	0	0	0	2	0	5	4	1	1	2
0	0	2	5	2	2	1	1	0	0	1	0	0	0	0	1	0	1	1	5	1	2	2	1
0	0	3	7	4	1	2	0	0	0	1	1	0	0	0	0	0	3	1	5	4	2	2	2
0	0	4	6	3	1	1	1	0	1	0	0	0	0	0	0	0	2	4	5	5	4	2	1
0	0	5	1	1	2	1	1	0	0	1	0	0	0	0	0	0	3	9	9	4	0	1	2
0	0	6	6	3	1	2	0	1	1	0	0	0	0	1	0	0	2	2	5	6	3	2	1
0	0	7	4	2	2	1	0	1	1	1	1	0	0	0	0	0	1	0	5	1	1	2	2
0	0	8	7	4	2	3	0	1	1	0	0	0	0	0	0	0	2	0	0	3	1	1	2
0	0	9	6	3	1	1	0	0	0	0	0	0	1	1	0	0	4	5	5	4	5	2	3
0	1	0	8	5	2	2	0	0	0	1	0	0	0	0	0	0	3	1	5	3	2	3	2
0	1	1	6	3	1	2	0	1	1	0	0	0	0	0	0	0	2	1	0	5	1	2	2
0	1	2	6	3	1	1	0	0	1	1	0	0	0	0	0	0	2	7	0	4	5	2	1
0	1	3	8	5	2	1	0	0	0	1	1	0	0	0	0	0	2	0	5	2	1	2	1
0	1	4	1	1	1	4	1	1	1	1	0	0	0	0	0	0	1	0	5	2	1	2	2
0	1	5	1	1	2	1	0	0	0	0	0	0	1	1	0	0	2	1	5	3	2	2	2
0	1	6	2	1	1	5	1	1	1	0	0	0	0	0	0	0	2	0	5	4	1	2	2
0	1	7	4	2	2	1	0	1	0	1	0	0	0	0	0	0	3	0	5	3	1	2	2
0	1	8	7	4	2	2	0	0	0	1	0	0	0	0	0	0	2	0	0	5	1	2	2
0	1	9	3	1	1	1	0	1	1	0	0	0	0	0	0	0	1	1	5	3	2	2	1
0	2	0	5	2	1	3	0	0	0	1	0	0	0	0	0	0	2	1	5	4	2	2	2

Table 2 Coded data from 20 questionnaires

§8.3 ONE-WAY FREQUENCY COUNTS

8.6 The first type of question invariably asked of survey data is how many...?

"How many people said they were satisfied with the clinic's signposting", "how many were attending for the first time"... etc..

These are answered by summarising the replies to relevant questions and producing what statisticians call 1–way frequency counts.

8.7 In most surveys they will be used first to test the representativeness of the sample against known data. For example, in our demonstration survey, out patient records show that women account for approximately 60% of all appointments. Counting down column 6 (Table 2) produces 10 code "1"s and 10 "2"s, equal numbers of women and men, but the sample as a whole contained 62% (226) women—close enough to the official figure to assume that the sample is not gender biased. The comparison could be presented in a simple table, or included as percentages in the text.

	1986/7 Survey data	Clinic sample
WOMEN	59.3%	62%
MEN	40.7%	38%
	N=27,000	N=365

Table 3

8.8 Most 1–way counts will be used to summarise your data. Many surveys do this for every question and it is customary to include a complete set of counts as an appendix to the full report. A quick, but rather illegible method is to present the results on a blank questionnaire. This is just about acceptable in an appendix, but should avoided as the main method for presenting results in the body of the report.

Presenting one-way counts

8.9 How you present the results will depend on the type and complexity of the question, and on how far you want to highlight the results.

8.10 Frequency tables are clear, informative and dull. The results of question—"mode of travel to clinic" could be shown as a table.

	%
Car	49
Bus	27
Hospital car	11
Ambulance	4
Other	9

Table 4. Mode of travel to clinic (N=365)

8.11 The numbers in each category should normally be expressed as a percentage—unless so small as to make percentaging ridiculous. The total number to which the table applies should always be given on every table—important since different tables in the same survey can have different bases. There is then no need to put the absolute numbers against each category and the table is kept clear and simple. So simple, that many of these results could just as clearly be written into the text.

Missing data

	%	Corrected %
Car	45	49
Bus	25	27
Hospital car	10	11
Ambulance	4	4
Other	8	9
Missing	8	–
	N=365	N=336

Table 5. Mode of travel to clinic

8.12 It is not unusual to find questions being accidentally or intentionally missed and you should always state on how many valid cases each analysis is based. But unless you want to emphasise the number of missing replies to a question, use only the corrected percentages, and give the new total.

Graphical presentations of one-way results

8.13 Pie and bar charts are two graphical ways of presenting one-way counts. But both should be used sparingly as they take-up more space than a table.

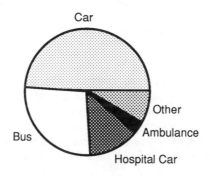

Fig.1 Mode of Travel to Clinic

8.14 Bar charts can be arranged vertically or horizontally—arguably, the former stresses the differences between categories.

Fig.2 Mode of Travel to Clinic
(Vertical Bar-chart)

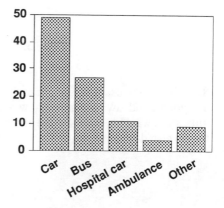

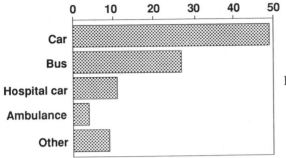

Fig.3 Mode of Travel to Clinic
(Horizontal Bar-chart)

§8.4 COMPARING REPLIES TO SEVERAL QUESTIONS

8.15 Most one-way methods are easily adapted to show the results of several questions simultaneously. Question 2 needs such a method because it is in fact 10 separate questions, masquerading as one. It is equivalent to asking:

Did you find the out-patients department welcoming   YES/NO

Did you find the out-patients department comfortable YES/NO

etc..

As 10 separate questions, it needs 10 separate data columns. (See Table 2)

8.16 This type of unconstrained multiple choice question ("circle as many as you wish") should generally be avoided. They take up data space, much of it void; they give no sense of a respondent's priorities; they do not show whether the respondents have considered all the options; and they can be difficult to analyse.

8.17 These ten questions can be summarised in a single table (Table 6), or more strikingly compared with a bar chart (Figures 4 and 5).

79

Table 6. Atmosphere in the out patients department

	No. of respondents	% of sample (N=365)
Welcoming	91	25
Comfortable	153	42
Pleasant	172	47
Efficient	201	55
Clinical	55	15
Disorganised	7	2
Confusing	29	8
Frustrating	55	15
Like a railway station	11	3
Total replies	N=774	

§8.5 SUMMARISING SCALED QUESTIONS

8.18 Shades of opinion, rather than simple YES/NO answers, can be got by using scaled questions.

Thinking about the Health Service in Thursby, do you feel the service offered is:

Very good	Good	Average	Poor	Very Poor
❑	❑	❑	❑	❑

8.19 Such questions are more difficult to design than they at first appear. It is hard to devise categories which are relevant to the topic, and also to frame the question so that a majority don't automatically tick the first positive category, in this case "Good (2)."

8.20 Should there be an even or odd number of categories? Odds, usually 5, are more common, but choose an even number if you want to force respondents into expressing positive or negative opinions. Results can be presented as tables of percentages, or as histograms.

Indices/indexation

8.21 Indices provide an even more economical presentation. Each point on the scale is given a score (often 1–5). These are added for all respondents and either reported as an average, or divided by the maximum possible scores to give a number between 0 and 1.

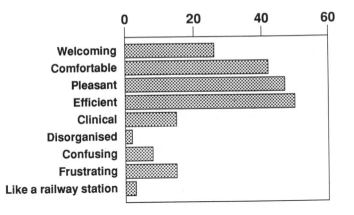

Fig.4 Atmosphere in Out-Patients

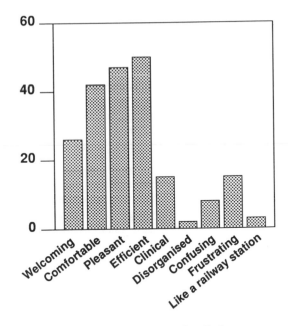

Fig.5 Atmosphere in Out-Patients

8.22 Though widely used, they are open to important objections. Firstly that the scores given to the scale points are entirely arbitrary. Why use 1,2,3,4,5—equal intervals—when there is no corroborating evidence that respondents perceive the differences between the categories as equal? Do people really think that the difference between a very good and good health service is the same as that between average and poor, or twice that between average and very poor? Showing the results as a histogram makes no assumptions about these differences—summarising them as an index assumes they can be meaningfully represented as numerical and equal.

8.23 Careful piloting may be able to produce categories which are fairly evenly spaced for most respondents. The HPAU questionnaire seems to be trying to do this when it replaces the usual scale points "very good... etc." with responses nearer to what patients might say or think.

8.24 Whether or not it is reasonable to assume that the categories are evenly spaced, any summarising measure is also open to the objection that it reduces several different patterns to a similar index value. In extreme cases, the same index value can stand for very different response patterns—all four charts 6A–6D summarise to the same value 0.78, or a mean reply of 3.9.

8.25 Many researchers are prepared to overlook these objections when indices are only being used to present the results from single questions. But indexation becomes far more contentious when it tries to combine the results of several questions. There are two common forms. Firstly when replies to several questions are aggregated to give an overall evaluation of some aspect of health services. Typically, replies to questions on ward facilities, comfort etc. might be combined into an overall evaluation of the ward. Again, the obvious objection is that no account is taken of patient priorities in combining this data. The indexation almost always assumes that patients regard all aspects as of equal importance—which they clearly don't.

8.26 A second type of indexation combines replies to often disparate questions, claiming these are measures of some underlying, but unstated, evaluative notion. It would have typically been discovered by large scale correlational analysis, which also provides numerical weights which are supposed to reflect the varying importance of the different questions to the basic concept. If used at all, such methods need a great deal of circumspection and statistical expertise. Like many others, Cartwright is very wary of these practices:

> "I am particularly suspicious of factor analyses in which responses to a series of questions are combined in elaborate exercises with dubious statistical validity and then given pretentious labels. Such techniques may be particularly tempting to researchers dealing with responses to questions of little interest and concern to the people being interviewed . . ." (Cartwright 1988)

82

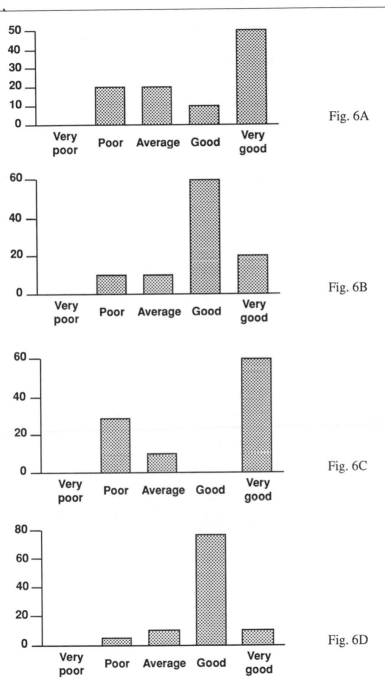

Fig. 6A

Fig. 6B

Fig. 6C

Fig. 6D

§8.6 SUMMARISING AND PRE-CODING NUMERICAL DATA

8.27 Consumer feedback studies may include a few questions which collect numerical data. For example (Qn.4):

> How long did you wait before first seeing a doctor or nurse after giving your name to Reception?
>
> ....minutes

8.28 There are several standard ways of presenting this data. It can be coded into suitable intervals and presented as a table, bar chart or any of the other methods used for categorical data.

Waiting time	% of sample
No wait	11
5 mins.	29
10 mins.	10
15 mins.	27
20–44 mins.	5
45+ mins.	18
	(N=365)

Table 7

8.29 Numerical data can also be averaged— by adding all observations and dividing by the total number of observations (Statistically this is known as the "mean"). The mean for this data is 19.2 minutes.

8.30 The work of post-coding can be avoided if suitable categories are built into the question. Choosing them is not always easy and often requires extensive piloting. Try to avoid categories which are too broad, when all respondents give the same reply, and those which are too narrow, with very small numbers in each. Most surveys aim to keep to a reasonable number of categories, say 4 or 5 which are defined so that each get roughly the same number of replies. A question on waiting time could be pre-coded as follows:

> When you arrived, how long did you think you would have to wait?
>
> No idea ❏
>
> Less than 5 minutes ❏

6–10 minutes	❏
11–15 minutes	❏
16–20 minutes	❏
21–45 minutes	❏
46 and over	❏

8.31 These categories can be confusing for respondents who tend to give answers to the nearest 5, 10 or 15 minutes and can lead to inaccurate data. For example, which of the above would be most appropriate for someone who expected to wait about 15 minutes? Other intervals can be less ambiguous.

How long was it before you were actually seen?

1–12 minutes	❏
13–22 minutes	❏
23–37 minutes	❏
38–50 minutes	❏
51 and over	❏

8.32 Data collected in category form can still be converted to averages, by multiplying the number of respondents in each category by the value of its midpoint. But this is impossible if the highest value category is open-ended. If you want to recombine categorical data into averages make sure that categories such as "51 minutes and over" are replaced with fixed intervals: 1–2hours; over2–3; over3–4.. to the point where every respondent is catered for.

§8.7 RELATIONSHIPS BETWEEN REPLIES

8.33 So far, this section has only dealt with methods for summarising the data from individual questions—different techniques are needed to analyse the relationship between the replies to two or more questions. You will need such techniques to report on issues such as:

- were there differences between separate wards and clinics
- were men happier than women with the toilet and washing facilities
- did the people to had to travel furthest to out patient clinics arrive the earliest
- were smokers as prepared as non-smokers to accept restrictions on smoking?

Example—Differences between waiting areas

8.34 Question 7 records views on the temperature in the clinic waiting rooms (coded in column 23 on the data grid—Table 2). Column 5 contains a code for the waiting area. To answer the question: were there any differences between areas, you will need to:

- draw a grid showing the categories of the two variables adding an extra row and column for the marginals.

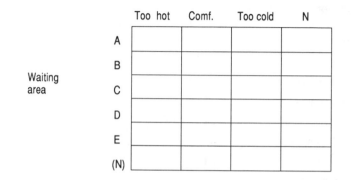

- simultaneously move down the two relevant columns on the data table (col. 5 & 23) marking each combination on the grid

- total the number in each grid square

- add across the rows and down the columns, putting the row and column totals in the spare cells (these are the marginals).

This is a table of frequencies.

8.35 To answer the question—"were there differences between waiting areas" you need to know what proportion of people in each area gave the different responses. You need to calculate the row percentages.

| Waiting area | Percentage in each area saying Temperature was: | | | N | total |
	Too hot	Comfortable	Too cold		
A	13.2	85.8	0.9	106	29.0
B	11.5	76.9	11.5	78	21.4
C	9.6	85.1	5.3	94	25.8
D	10.3	84.4	5.2	58	15.9
E	17.2	75.9	6.9	29	7.9

Table 8   Responses to temperature of different waiting areas

8.36 Various charts such as stacked (Fig.7A) and overlaid (Fig.7B) bar charts will convey the same information.

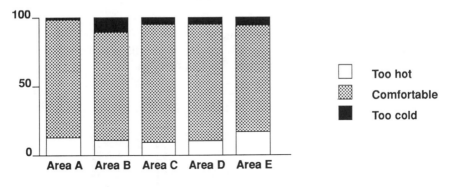

Fig. 7A Temperature in waiting areas

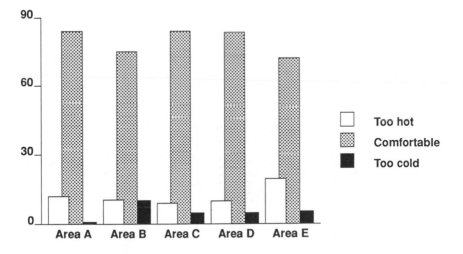

Fig. 7B Temperature in waiting areas

It is reasonably clear the the people in waiting areas B and E were less satisfied with the temperature. The result merits investigation.

8.37 The same basic type of table (a contingency table) can be used to answer a question such as: was there any connection between the time people had to wait and their opinion of their overall treatment (Qns.4 & 8)

Table 9

Percentage of people expressing different levels of satisfaction with their overall treatment, by waiting time.

Waiting time	Very satisfied	Quite satisfied	Not satisfied	N	% of total
No wait	75.8	22.5	2.5	40	11
5 mins.	72.6	23.6	3.8	106	29
10 mins.	63.9	27.8	8.3	36	10
15 mins.	60.6	32.3	7.1	99	27
20–44mins.	55.5	33.3	11.1	18	5
45&over	53.0	33.3	13.6	66	18
N	235	104	26	365	
% of total	64.3	29.0	7.0		100

8.38 We see that the proportion in the "very satisfied" column increases with reduced waiting time (from 53–75.8%); and in the "not satisfied" column increases with the wait. The trend is very nearly perfect and quite marked in the "not satisfied" column.

8.39 Again, this trend can be represented by various charts (see figures 8A and 8B.

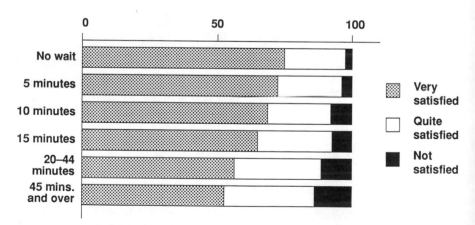

Fig. 8A Waiting time vs. satisfaction with treatment

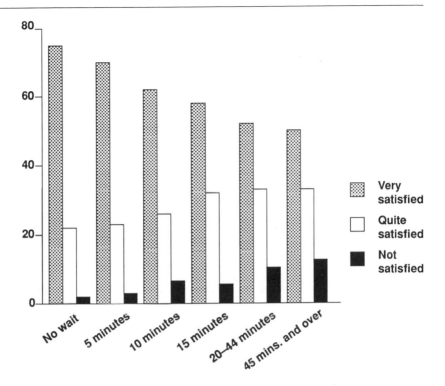

Fig. 8B Waiting time vs. satisfaction with treatment

8.40 From this, albeit fictional, data, there would be strong evidence of a association. One would want to carry out further research, perhaps open-ended interviews, to confirm that the link was causal—that is, to find out what particular aspects of waiting patients disliked and how these impinged on their views of the treatment received. Such additional research, or some strong intuitive argument, is always needed to support associations which in themselves are no guarantee of causation.

§8.8 STATISTICAL TESTS

8.41 Both the previous examples contain results which seem to justify investigation, but can statistical tests help confirm this, by reporting the quantitative significance of any differences or trends? The most common way of assessing whether or not there is any association in a contingency table is the chi-squared test. It is valid for all tables provided:

- none of the entries are 0
- in a 2-cell table, both "expected" frequencies are greater than 4
- in a larger table, not more than 20% of "expected" frequencies are less than 5.

8.42 Chi-squared addresses questions of the form—what is the likelihood of getting a table containing these apparent differences if there really are none. It works by summing the squared differences of the values actually present in each cell from that which would be "expected" if respondents were simply assigned to cells by chance. The larger the value, the greater the likelihood of there being some significant differences. A statistical estimate of this likelihood can be had by looking up the computed value of chi-squared in published tables.

| Waiting area | Number saying temperature was: | | | N | % of total |
	Too hot	Comfortable	Too cold		
A	14	91	1	106	29.0
B	9	60	9	78	21.4
C	9	80	5	94	25.8
D	6	49	3	58	15.9
E	5	22	2	29	7.9
	43	302	20	365	
	11.8	82.7	5.5		100.0

8.43 If there were no connection between where one waited and one's views on the temperature, then the expected number giving a particular view, in a particular area, would simply be the proportion in that area, times the proportion giving that view overall, times the number in the sample. So the expected number saying waiting area A is too hot would be:

$$\frac{43}{365} \times \frac{106}{365} \times 365 = 12.49$$

Chi-squared is the sum of the squared differences between the actual and expected values, divided in each case by the expected values:

$$\chi^2 = \sum \frac{(O-E)^2}{E} = \frac{(14-12.49)^2}{12.49} + \frac{(91-87.7)^2}{87.7} + \ldots = 11.44$$

From published values, this figure for chi-squared occurs in a 5x3 table with a probability of around 15% even when there is no relation between the two factors. Statisticians would probably want a higher value, giving a probability of 5 or 10%, before regarding any trend or differences as notable.

8.44 Chi-squared is a robust test, there are relatively few restrictions on its use, but it is also insensitive. Here, it has tested for all possible differences between clinics, and the overall value is quite low because there are barely any differences within the groups, A,C & D and B & E. Chi-squared has not been sufficiently sensitive to draw attention to the differences *between* these groups, even though they are clearly visible. By only using chi-squared, and not looking at the table, we could have easily overlooked what differences there were.

8.45 The same insensitivity is revealed when chi-squared is applied to table 9 (Waiting times vs. satisfaction levels). Here the value is 13.2, around the 10% mark. Though a slightly better result, it is nothing like as significant as one would expect given the near perfect correlation.

8.46 The weakness here is that chi-squared is a measure of overall differences, and takes no account of the order of categories. The Kolmogorov-Smirnov test is much more suitable for tables where one or both axes are ordered and returns a value of .19, likely to occur in far less than 1% of cases if there were no associations. Kolmogorov-Smirnov compares the expected and actual cumulative frequencies, the order in which they are summed being part of the null hypothesis. The test is therefore highly order dependent.

Which test?

8.47 Because most statistical tests were developed for physical and other types of data which are capable of continuous measurement, they are generally unsuitable for the categorical data in most social surveys. A very limited number of tests can be used on contingency tables—the best known are:

- Binomial test (2–cell tables only)

- Chi-squared test (all tables, but invalid if frequencies are too small)

- Kologorov-Smirnov(tables in which the categories of one or both variables are naturally ordered)

8.48 As the above examples have shown, tests need to be chosen carefully and, even then, can overlook important results. If the trends or differences are very striking, the tests should confirm the obvious,but don't expect them to reveal results which are not immediately visible.

§8.9 COMPUTER DATA ANALYSIS

8.49 The examples so far have assumed an analysis done by hand from a data grid—only feasible with certain types of quite small surveys (Chapter 6 gives guidelines on when this is possible). The majority of surveys will be analysed by computer, normally in one of two ways.

1. Using an office database
2. Using a specialised survey analysis package

Analysis on an office database

8.50 Office databases are primarily concerned with storing and retrieving data on individual cases/records, not with summarising the information in sets of records. To do the sorts of analyses needed for a social survey, you will often need a supplementary graphs or charts utility, which may only be capable of producing one-way frequency counts. Only careful checking will tell if a package is suitable. Price and complexity are certainly no guide. The more expensive packages, especially any which describe themselves as "relational", keep their data in structures which are not amenable to simple summary. Even with a suitable package, you may have to save intermediate files and transfer them to the graphs utility.

Analysis with a survey package

8.51 SPSS is the best known of the specialised survey analysis packages. Previously confined to mainframes, it has recently been released in an IBM PC version (only compatible with the more powerful models) and looks to become even more widely used. Anyone planning their own computer analysis would do well to become familiar with this package. Both official and unofficial manuals are available, but the package has sufficient idiosyncrasies that it might be worth asking someone to help you get started.

8.52 To use SPSS, you will have to enter 3 types of information:

(i) *Data.*
Which can be supplied as a block of numbers, or in the most recent versions and SPSS–PC, typed onto a form-entry screen.

(ii) *Data definition information.* (The Data Specifications.)
Either supplied in a separate file, or in response to the prompts of SPSS-PC. It must be supplied in a very specific format and give the package information such as: how many variables you have; what you want to call them "AGE GENDER

CLINIC etc."; in which columns it can find the data corresponding to each variable; and, whether the data is entirely numeric or includes alphabetic characters. You also have the option of supplying detailed codebook information, such as giving labels to the codes to dramatically improve the legibility of tables.

This information obviously multiplies with the number of questions and codes, and a complete data definition file for a 15 page questionnaire could complete be 30–40,000 characters long and take several days to devise.

(iii) *Analyses requests* (The Control File)

Finally you will have to specify the analyses you want. After the effort of entering the data and the definition file this is distinctly anti-climactic. In most versions of SPSS, something akin to the 14 character command: "FREQUENCIES ALL" will produce 1–way frequency tables for *all* your variables—though you may want to vary the output format option for different sets of variables.

8.53 Frequency analysis will be done in a matter of seconds, or at most a few minutes for a large data set. Crosstabulations can be obtained almost as quickly. In computer analysis almost all the work goes into entering the data and data definitions and then interpreting large quantities of print-out. Apart from the speed of analysis, a package such as SPSS can produce tables and graphs in a form directly suitable for reports, or for editing with an office word-processor. Anyone who has toiled over re-typing tables, or hand-drawn graphs will immediately recognise the value of such facilities.

Computer analysis—some drawbacks

8.54 For experienced researchers, a well-designed, dedicated survey analysis package is a godsend. For novices, the initial training time—will the survey get done on time?—is worrying, but usually rewarding. The danger with all such packages is their tendency to encourage the "more analysis = better results" syndrome. Cartwright, quoted above, has given her own pithy critique.

8.55 Two of the more tempting procedures, factor and canonical analyses, are complex tools limited to specific types of data and only capable of supplying tentative correlational ideas, not definitive causal results. So far, there is less evidence of their misuse in customer feedback surveys, than there is in other areas of social research, but as cheaper packages and a new generation of micros make them available to more statistical novices, so the risk is bound to increase.

In summary

- most survey data can be analysed without any statistical expertise
- simple analysis techniques are nearly always best
- the analysis should be a process of asking pre-defined questions of your data, and not of trying different analytical techniques in the hope of finding results
- most of your data will be summarised with 1–way frequency counts, which can be reported as frequency tables or various graphical methods such as pie and bar charts
- scaled questions are often summarised as indices, but this should be done with some caution
- exploring correlations between the sorts of data collected in social surveys is almost always best done with crosstabulations
- few statistical tests are suitable, and those that are need careful use and are unlikely to add much. They are best avoided
- in a computerised data analysis, preparing and entering the data, and setting up the data definitions, is likely to take much longer than the analysis itself
- do not expect an office database package to be immediately suitable for survey analysis. At the very least you may need a supplementary graphs and charts utility
- the more elaborate packages are less likely to be suitable
- specialised survey packages will save a great deal of time and effort, and do everything you need, but they are quite expensive and run on only the more powerful micros. Novices will find them laborious but not difficult to learn
- computer analysis brings its own dangers—encouraging over analysis and the use of techniques which are not fully understood and do nothing but confuse the issues

9. DOING A SURVEY

§9.1 INTRODUCTION

9.1 How long will your survey take; how much will it cost; what other resources are needed; and what are the likely snags? These are some of the very practical questions this section tries to answer by describing the typical timetables and stages of two pieces of research—the first, a medium sized population survey; the second, a low-budget hospital food survey. Although you may not be intending to do either of these, the practical details, timetables and costings may still be helpful.

§9.2 A POPULATION SURVEY

9.2 After extensive discussions with unit and general management, your district management service support unit gets approval to investigate local views on the health services in a town of 100,000 inhabitants.

9.3 You look at a few similar studies; talk to the local Planning Department, who had recently done a similar sized survey on housing conditions; and also to social researchers at a local university, who were unable to offer practical help beyond general advice. You finally decide to conduct an interview based population study on 1500–2000 households. You reject the cheaper option of a mailed questionnaire as it could not collect sufficiently detailed information, and might give an unacceptably low response rate.

9.4 Once the basic design has been agreed, the research might proceed as follows.

Recruiting interviewers

9.5 Your local university knows of a small pool of experienced interviewers, but they still need training on your questionnaire, and most are only available part-time. The number of interviewers required will depend on how the sample is to be drawn, and you are still undecided whether to use the Register of Electors, or get interviewers to do the sampling by selecting every 'n'th. household in designated streets. If you draw names from the Register, you need to allow at least 3hrs. per interview—to cover interviewer travel time and return visits when respondents are out or unavailable. In these circumstances, a single interviewer would be unlikely to do more than 10 interviews per week. A further point against the Register is that it is known to be unreliable in at least two of the central urban areas which you want to cover.

9.6 Sampling by addresses/households in designated streets reduces interviewer travel and call-back time, and your interviewers can manage as many as 4–5 interviews per day. You decide to adopt this method. But there is still the problem of finding people in. You are reluctant to adopt too liberal a replacement strategy, and insist that your interviewers make four attempts to contact a household, including one evening and one weekend visit, before replacing it with its neighbours.

9.7 You want the interviewing to be completed in 3 months. 15 interviewers, might manage 1500 interviews in that time, but recruiting a further 5 or 10 would be safer. This will mean newspaper advertisements; corresponding with several hundred applicants; arranging recruitment interviews etc. A full-time fieldwork supervisor will be needed, for at least one month of interviewer recruitment and training and 2–3 months of fieldwork.

Drawing the sample

9.8 You already have an idea of the areas and streets to be covered, but you need to know the approximate number of households in these streets. Your interviewers are asked to estimate this number by going through the Register and counting the number of households. These estimates are confirmed by interviewers visiting the relevant streets and noting addresses which are unoccupied, have changed to multiple occupancy, or are otherwise likely to contain a different number of households from those recorded in the Register.

Questionnaire design

9.9 You have found an existing questionnaire with many suitable questions, but want to add some topics and improve the filtering. Having to design a questionnaire from scratch would have taken several weeks. Your alterations only take 4 days, but you decide to ask a local academic with relevant research experience to assess every question. You take her advice and make several further changes. The entire process, including typing, takes just over a fortnight.

Piloting the questionnaire

9.10 To clean up the sequencing, wording, layout etc.. you need at least 30 pilot interviews by several interviewers. You use both inexperienced and experienced interviewers, and select a wide range of respondents. Time is allowed for interviewer debriefing—each of them is taken through a sample of their questionnaires. You check that both interviewers and respondents are making sense of the questions and respondents are not being asked to give details which tax their memory.

9.11 Fortunately, you decide not to develop any new pre-coded questions. If you had, this could have involved an open-ended pre-pilot, and a subsequent pilot on the draft pre-codes.

Pilot analysis

9.12 Once you have the final version of the questionnaire, you do a further pilot of 30. Some of the key data is analysed by hand. You are not entirely satisfied with the results—the questions do not collect precisely the information needed, but you decide to go ahead nonetheless.

Training the interviewers

9.13 Some of the interviewers have already helped with the piloting, but all will need training at some stage. A training programme for each group of ten interviewers takes 2–3 days and is especially important as you want your interviewers to do some of the coding during the interview. To check that interviewers are managing satisfactorily, you try to arrange for a researcher to accompany them for their first few interviews.

Typing and Printing

9.14 Long questionnaires are very time consuming to type and lay out, and preparations and printing costs are not insignificant. Your 15–20 page questionnaire will take an absolute minimum of 3 person-days to lay out and it is safer to allow nearer 5 when there are complex option paths and elaborate multiple choice questions. With its filter systems and layout suitable for direct entry, your questionnaire takes nearly a week to type and design. Fortunately, one of your team has layout/graphics skills.

9.15 Your pilot schedules will be xeroxed, but to save money in the main survey, 2000 offset copies are done from your own artwork. The final art work and printing takes 3 weeks. Apart from the questionnaire, you also have to produce: interviewer identification cards, letters of introduction, prompt cards etc.

Fieldwork data-preparation

9.16 Although some of your interviewers would have preferred it, you decide against pre-arranging interviews, as this tends to reduce the response rate and incurs postage and phone bills.

The fieldwork eventually starts.

9.17 In a modest population survey, the coding and data preparation falls into 5 main phases:

1. Monitoring questionnaire returns—numbering, bundling etc. This could be done by the fieldwork supervisor.
2. Supervising the interviewers—arrange regular debriefing sessions and group meetings.
3. Checking, editing and post-coding. After the first hundred or so interviews are completed, sufficient data is available to devise categories for the few remaining uncoded questions. As you are not using separate coding sheets, open-ended answers are coded on the questionnaires. Questionnaires are checked for incompleteness, invalid responses etc., by a small group of trained checker/coders. The 15 page questionnaires take 15–20 minutes each for coding, editing, and general tidying-up.
4. Data entry. You plan to use the your office micro for data input. Each questionnaire generates 400 data characters. Keyboard operators reading directly from the questionnaires and taking frequent breaks, average about 12–15 questionnaires per hour. It will take between 120 and 150 hours to enter the data from the 1700 interviews. Neither the office micro, nor suitable staff are available for this amount of time during the research period—you therefore borrow a micro from another unit and employ someone to input approximately half the data.
5. Further data checking. Early on, you get each of your two typists to check the coding and re-enter the data on a small sample of the other's questionnaires. You repeat the exercise towards the end of the data entry. Neither check shows up any systematic errors.

Data Analysis

9.18 The analysis is to be done on the District mainframe running SPSS. Because the project is working to a tight timetable, the first three stages in the analysis have to be done at the same time as the data entry.

9.19 There are five stages:

1. Writing and entering the data specification/description file.

   You decide to include full codebook information to maximise the legibility of the output. Given the large number of variables and codes, the file is between 30,000 and 40,000 characters long, and takes an experienced survey analyst, and a proficient typist, several days to prepare.

2. Preparing and running logic and range checks.

   Reasonably extensive checks are carried out on batches of the data soon after it has been entered. Setting up the checks takes several days. Each set of checks on a batch of data takes a few hours.

3. Correcting the erroneous data.

   Most errors were eliminated in the preliminary manual checks, but the computerised logic and range checks have shown up a further 200 or so errors which need tracing and correcting. In many cases, the original questionnaires need consulting, so each error takes around 10 minutes to correct.

4. Running simple frequency counts on the full data.

   On the mainframe an experienced researcher should be able to do these basic analysis in a few hours and certainly in no more than two days.

5. Subsequent analyses.

9.20 Many of your questions are answered by the simple frequency counts, but you also want a number of crosstabulations, and consider using indices to summarise some of the health behaviour and attitude data. These additional analyses take 2 weeks.

9.21 Having done the analyses you can get an idea of how much it would have cost to do the work on another computer. The local university might have been able to help, provided an academic agrees to liaise with your project. You will have needed rather less than 1 hour of computer central processor time (£200 on a university machine); and will probably have to pay for media costs and a small contribution towards systems support—(also £200). Commercially, the costs will be well in excess of double this.

Reporting

9.22 Coming to grips with the large quantities of computer print-out, and preparing data tables and other quantitative displays for the report, takes much longer than you expected. If you had been able to afford SPSS–PC you would have been able to directly transfer its tables and other charts to your office word-processor, but, with SPSS on the mainframe, most of these have to to be re-typed.

9.23 You find yourself getting interested in some of the patterns which are showing up in the results and the report writing gets extended as you explore interesting correlations, develop and address hypotheses, and tackle matters of policy. You keep going back to the print-out and run several more analyses. Although a simple descriptive report could have been written in a week, you find you need at least a month and then rather longer to turn the conclusions into policy proposals.

9.24 You end up preparing 3 separate reports: a list of the recommendations, accompanied by a brief summary of the project, for circulation to Authority members and most management; a full report—details of the work, main results and recommendations, for more limited circulation; and a statistical appendix including further details of methods. The report is discussed by District General Management and the Authority—a gloss of selected findings is issued to the press. Many of your recommendations, including changes to clinic opening hours, hospital transport, and patient information booklets are to be implemented over the next year—other proposals, to move and reorganise clinics are to be fed into the long term planning process. Various Unit Managers get involved with the proposals. Contacts are also made with the Local Authority to explore the possibilities of a health awareness campaign. The project looks likely to have wide implications for patterns of local health provision.

9.25 The project has taken 11.5 months, after the initial decision to pursue the study seriously. Had there been any delays: due to illness, computer breakdown, difficulties with the fieldwork or coding, it would have taken longer.

The eventual timetable

Preliminary discussion and outline proposal	2 months
Drawing-up a research specification; talking to the L.A. Planning Dept.; academics etc..; obtaining copies of research done by other DHAs.. Writing a detailed proposal Deciding to do the research in-house Getting funds approved (your funders want the money to be spent within the next financial year - and your unit manager will only release you for the same period)	3 months
Recruiting a fieldwork supervisor Recruiting interviewers Modifying an existing questionnaire Piloting the modifications (twice) Drawing the sample	2.5 months
Fieldwork Finalising a coding scheme Coding and entering the data Some checking of data entry and coding	3 months
Further data input and checking Constructing the data definition file and setting-up the first analyses	1 month
Bulk of the analysis Reporting	2 months

Costs

You approach a Polytechnic department which has a group of workers used to doing this type of health population study—they quote the following costs. Small independent academic research groups would charge much the same; large commercial organisations, if they have the relevant expertise, will cost considerably more.

Costs are at 1987 rates.

Survey Costing—One Borough

Enumeration: 150 ED's @ £15	£ 2,500
Fieldwork: 1500 interviews @ £7	£10,500
Interviewer's travel £12.50 by 20 by 12 weeks	£ 3,000
Fieldwork supervisor's salary £200 x 15 weeks	£ 3,000
Fieldwork supervisor's travel £20 x 15 weeks	£ 300
Printing: 2000 @ 80p. + 15% VAT	£ 1,150
Computing—labour 150 hours @ £15	£ 2,250
Computing—machine use 60 hours @ £5	£ 300
Typing	£ 1,200
Misc. expenses	£ 500
Consultants travel £15 x 3 x 25 weeks	£ 1,125
	£26,515
Polytechnic Admin costs (22.5%)—covers supplying consultants & releasing them from other work	£ 5,965
Total	£32,680

§9.3 A HOSPITAL FOOD SURVEY

9.26 A much more modest survey. Several letters on hospital food appear in the local press and local radio runs a feature. You already have long-term plans for restructuring the facilities, but want to see if a small survey of patients can suggest interim improvements, as well as showing you are taking the matter seriously.

Preliminary design

9.27 You talk to catering management and supervisors to get a sense of the problems and the likely limits on making short-term changes. Ward sisters are asked their views and are generally supportive. Several CHC members offer help and show you a copy of a report, and questionnaire, from a similar survey in the neighbouring District.

Design

9.28 The study is based in a 500 bed general hospital; and you decide to do a one-off survey of all the patients. Approximately 400 beds are occupied. Previous surveys suggest that around 100 patients will either be too ill or otherwise unable to take part. You decide against the extra cost of Freepost envelopes and will rely on collection boxes in the wards. You hope to get between a 50% and 60% response rate.

9.29 The QA unit has a new office microcomputer (an IBM AT clone) and a commercial office database. It looks as though it should meet your basic analysis requirements.

9.30 After further discussions with the catering management and other interested parties, you focus the research on 3 areas: warmth of food; provision of special diets; and whether the menus had changed sufficiently to accommodate trends towards more fresh and wholefood diets.

9.31 You check with the York archive and Jones, Leneman and Maclean (1985). You identify 5 similar studies and write for copies.

9.32 From these, and your own questions, you compile a 15 section questionnaire with an average of 5 pre-coded questions per section. Perhaps a bit too long, but enabling you to research the three main areas in considerable detail, as well as collecting more general opinions on the catering.

Piloting

9.33 The draft questionnaire is typed and tested in two very different wards. Some patients find the questionnaire too complicated. You also ask several patients what they think of each of the questions—and get the opinions of catering management and the management services statistician.

9.34 A second version is produced and tested in one ward. With minor modifications, this becomes the final version. Including an introductory half-page explaining the project and saying how to return the questionnaire, the document is 4xA4 pages long and has space for open comments in all its sections. Because of the difficulties experienced by some of the respondents in the pilot study, you will try to arrange for researchers to be on hand to help.

9.35 You decide to xerox the questionnaire, because printing would be too expensive in a run of this length. But to make the copies more attractive, you use letraset and a cartoon on the front page.

Data collection

9.36 You remind the ward sisters of the project and arrange for collection boxes to be prominently situated. In most wards there is space to put a small sandwich-board poster next to the box. Putting other posters in the wards would be expensive and unproductive. Hospital radio runs a feature—you explain the project and ask for co-operation.

9.37 Helped by two of your staff and two CHC members you distribute questionnaires in all the wards. Ward sisters suggest you miss about 100 patients. Questionnaires are handed to patients individually, and you stop to explain the project and ask if people are likely to need any help. Only 15 patients refuse to take part. One of the group returns to the ward soon after, to help where needed.

9.38 Boxes are collected after 3 days. There are 205 usable questionnaires, a very respectable 68% of all those approached.

Data coding and entry

9.39 Six sections of the questionnaire have produced open comments from around 30% of respondents. You draw up a coding scheme for each of these, but decide to summarise the other comments manually and/or report them verbatim.

9.40 The pre-coded questions code into approximately 80 numbers—add another 6 for the open questions; a three digit questionnaire number; a few other pieces of classification information—and there are 100 numbers per questionnaire. The entire data set is therefore 20,500 digits.

9.41 Data entry will have to be done on the analysis micro, to which you only have limited access. Because the questionnaires are not very well set out for fast direct entry, and contain a considerable number of comments, you decide to use coding sheets. The distribution team agrees to help with the coding and a unit secretary is assigned the actual data input. Each completed questionnaire takes 5 minutes to code. Data is typed, as a grid, into a word-processing package on the analysis machine—it takes 5 days of the typists time. With some help, you are able to transfer it to the database and make sure two security copies are kept on floppy disc.

Data checks

9.42 Fifteen of the questionnaires are compared against the computer data file. There are a few, apparently random, errors, but nothing to warrant systematic investigation. The numbers on all the coding sheets are visually checked against a print-out of the data grid. A few more errors are found, but nothing systematic. All the errors found are corrected.

Analysis

9.43 You take a while to become familiar with the database package, though you have used other databases before. It will do simple frequency counts, and by judicious use of the "select cases" options and "graphs and charts" facilities, can provide results on sub-populations akin to crosstabulation. It does most of what you need, though the number of variables, 80+, might be better handled with a dedicated survey package.

9.44 Entering the field descriptions and titles takes nearly a day. The database accepts the data from the word-processor file. Frequency counts are done for all the questions and take two days. You also select some of the more obvious sub-samples to see how their results differ. You are beginning to get the basis for a report.

Reporting and further analysis

9.45 Other pressures on your time, and the QA unit wanting its computer, extend the period of analysis and reporting. You provide a summary of the main results—including the views of distinct groups of patients. Based on the replies to the more focused questions and the open comments you are able to make a number of comments which seem likely to be noted. The 20 page report and a 2–page summary are quite widely circulated. A briefly annotated statistical summary is also given to relevant management. You also give several presentations on the findings.

9.46 Six months later, Catering management are exploring ways of improving the range of food and special diet provision. They are also liasing with Unit and General management on ways of altering meal times. News of probable changes are released to the local press.

The Eventual Timetable

9.47 Even as the main researcher, you have not been able to work full-time on the project. Some stages would have been quicker if you had, but the fieldwork and data entry would have taken much the same time.

9.48 It takes just over 5 months.

Preliminary discussions	1 month
Drawing-up a research specification; obtaining copies of research done by other DHAs.. Drafting a questionnaire	1 month
2 pilot runs Liaising with ward staff and generally arranging the data collection	1 month
Data collection	2 weeks
Coding and entering the data Some checking of data entry and coding	3 weeks
Analysis & Reporting	1 month

Costs

9.49 Here is an estimate of costs

Preparing and piloting draft questionnaires	£20
Xeroxing 400 @ 20p.	£80
Floppy discs	£10
Other xeroxing—coding sheets etc	£20
Xeroxing reports 30 @ £1.20	£36
Total	£166

Hidden Costs

9.50 A considerable amount of management and office staff time has been taken up by this survey. Consultants have even been known to run in-house patient feedback surveys. If their time is costed, it may have been cheaper to employ specialised survey workers and part-time clerical staff.

10.GETTING HELP

10.1 The help you get with a survey, can range from informal free advice to commissioning an entire project. This section lists some of the main sources and groups you may find helpful.

§10.1 FINDING SIMILAR STUDIES

10.2 Reading reports of similar studies can be a great help in planning a project. You should be able to find something suitable from the following indexes and reviews.

(i)   Jones et al. *Consumer Feedback* is the most comprehensive review to date. As well as work by DHAs and CHCs, it includes a few national TV and newspaper surveys and the relatively few academic excursions into feedback research. The review concentrates more on what was done, rather than how, though it has a useful chapter on methodology. As well as reviewing individual studies it summarises what was found on the various topics and highlights some areas which remain under-researched.

(ii) Cartwright's *Health Surveys in Practice and Potential* does very much what its secondary title suggests, i.e. "gives a critical review of (their) scope and methods." The surveys in question are mainly academic works and mainly conducted by interview, but studies done by CHCs and DHAs are given more than a passing mention. It has many helpful comments on survey methods and should be essential reading.

(iii) National Association of Health Authorities *NAHA Index of Consumer Relations in the NHS (1985)*—an annotated index of 93 consumer relations initiatives—many of them feedback surveys.

(iv) Centre for Health Economics (York University)—holds *The York Consumer Information Base,* a computerised database currently containing information on some 300 reported studies—almost all done by DHAs and CHCs. 20 items of data are kept on each study, including: summaries of its methods; aims and conclusions, plus the address of the commissioning authority. Access is currently limited, but the base is being developed for public use. (The Introduction to Booklet III in this series gives a few more details).

10.3 There is clearly a need for some centralised archive of feedback studies—several DHAs and CHCs have become victims of their own success and have had to devote considerable time to copying, distributing and generally answering queries on some of the better known studies. Some have even been forced to withdraw reports for this reason.

§10.2 TEXTS ON SURVEY METHODS

10.4 Anyone contemplating running a survey should have read:

Moser and Kalton *Survey Methods in Social Investigation*
and
McCrossan *A Handbook for Interviewers*

10.5 Both Jones and Cartwright give essential details specific to consumer feedback research in the NHS, as does the article by French (1981). The International Hospital Federation provides a concise and informative guide to both the issues and methods in patient feedback research:

IHF *And What Would They Know About It* (1988)

10.6 Beyond these, textbook on survey methods come and go with amazing rapidity. Two of the longer lived works which are both readable and practical are:

Gardner *Social Surveys for Social Planners*
Hoinville et al. *Survey Research Practice*

Though you may well have a favourite which is neither of these.

10.7 An interesting account of the practical hazards of large scale research is given by:

Maclean and Genn *Methodological Issues in Social Surveys*

There are also very many specialist texts giving detailed advice on different aspects of surveys.

§10.3 COMMISSIONING RESEARCH

10.8 A real minefield—you probably need all the skills to be able to do the research yourself, plus practical experience of research and commissioning to survive the process. The Social Research Association 1985 Conference Proceeding *Can You Buy It Off the Shelf?* is an invaluable, if discouraging, guide.

Who will do the research?

10.9 With patient feedback studies, you will probably be looking to one of the following three types of groups to do the work.

(1) A commercial market research organisation

There are unlikely to have extensive experience of patient feedback research; and the types of work they most often do—the general evaluation study—are those most fraught with difficulties. They do not always have a high standard of reporting, make little use of open comments and may try to convince you of the merits of large formal surveys when these are not what you need.

(2) Specialised socio-medical research units—either university based or independent charities.

These may either specialise in certain sorts of study, or be able to conduct a range of research. Different units have different house styles. From published work and advice of other DHAs you should get a reasonable sense of their respective merits and abilities. Beware of their trying to redefine your work to fit one of their standard research models, but otherwise you should at least be getting a known product from this source.

(3) Ad hoc research teams set up by free-lance researchers or academics.

These can range from semi-commercial free-lance outfits to university and polytechnic based academics using students as research workers. Costs will vary accordingly. Very cheap and resourceful work can be done, though make sure they contain at least someone with specialised knowledge of the research area who will have time to play a major role in the research.

How is it commissioned?

10.10 The research will probably be arranged through open or closed tender, or direct contract.

10.11 To openly tender, you publicly advertise for groups to apply to do your research. For all but the most mundane forms of market research this is very risky. Great skill and experience is needed to evaluate different applications and you may be up against the sales efforts of large market research groups. Costs will be difficult to compare, as different bases are often used. Many of the tendering groups will be unknown quantities and some serious research groups are unlikely to respond.

10.12 Closed tendering is slightly safer. You approach only those groups known to specialise in the type of work required. They will usually want to discuss the work with you before submitting a formal tender. There will still be difficulties evaluating proposals—and unless you are prepared to trust the design details to your contract researchers you will have to spend a not inconsiderable time drawing up a research specification. Again you should have someone with research experience and relevant skills on your side of any negotiations.

10.13 Placing a contract directly with a research agency of proven ability is one way of minimising the risks and your effort, but is arguably unjustified unless only one organisation is known to be capable of doing the desired research.

§10.4 OTHER TYPES OF HELP

10.14 Short of full-scale commissioning, various agencies and individuals may be able to help with different stages of a survey. Some of the main points at which you may want help are likely to be:

- Initial advice
- Research design/specification
- Drawing up a proposal
- Artwork on self-completion questionnaires
- Printing Interviewing
- Questionnaire distribution
- Data coding and entry
- Data analysis

Several different agencies have helped with this sort of research in the past.

CHCs

10.15 CHCs have been long-standing supporters of DHA research. They have provided individual expertise on research design; practical help with interviewing, questionnaire distribution and coding. CHC members with home micro's might be recruited to help with data entry, if not the actual analysis.

Manpower Services Commission

10.16 In its early days, the MSC job creation programmes provided the funds to employ both interviewers and researchers on DHA and CHC projects. Community Programme funds may also have been used for projects with a health research element. Authorities which do not have a policy of non-cooperation with the new Training Scheme might be able to arrange joint funded projects on which research workers get a significant training element—obviously this would be a matter for individual Authorities. Individuals might be able to do relevant research for an Authority and be paid under the Enterprise Allowance scheme, but this is well outside the spirit of its rules.

10.17 MSC funded ITECs may be prepared to provide greatly subsidised computer analysis facilities if the Authority has nothing suitable.

Charities and special patient groups

10.18 These may provide advice and helpers for projects on special needs groups.

Schools and 6th. form colleges

10.19 They have been known to help with data collection and analysis. GCSE sociology now has a big emphasis on project work. Some 6th. form colleges have very good computing facilities.

Community Associations

10.20 They have also helped with population studies, as have parish councils, local shops and various community members with an interest in the project. You might be able to recruit potential helpers through a public meeting or press advertisements.

Local media

10.21 The local press and radio may be able to help publicise a study.

Universities and polytechnics

10.22 Can provide a range of research support. Help given can range from conducting an entire project to advising on individual stages. But there are some important provisos. Unless you already have a named contact, finding appropriate faculty members may be surprisingly difficult. There are legal restrictions on the extent to which university resources can be used in doing unpaid research for outside bodies—though these are interpreted differently throughout institutions. You may be charged at something approaching commercial rates for, e.g. use of university computing facilities. Charges will be waived if the research is part of a teaching exercise, giving students experience in project work, or if it is part of the on-going personal research of a faculty member. Polytechnics are less restricted in the use of their finances for this sort of work, but local policy varies considerably.

10.23 One difficulty of relying on teaching faculty for extensive help is the number of other demands on their time during terms. Unless you can afford to fund a sabbatical, you will normally find the rate of research declining significantly during teaching periods. That said, it is usually worth exploring what these institutions can offer. Their sociology, social administration and management studies departments ought to be able to find someone who can give useful, and often free, advice.

10.24 They can also recommend students, at both undergraduate and research level, who would be prepared to do project work for you as an assessed part of their courses. Mature students, especially those with nursing qualifications, have been known to undertake major pieces of research and been very dedicated to their projects. Even if the scale of the research is limited by what an individual can achieve, their reports, with thorough discussions of methodology, reviews of relevant studies etc. can make a valuable contribution to planning future research.

10.25 Higher education institutions may also be able to offer groups of students, either to do entire projects, or to help with particular activities such as coding and data collection. Do not expect especially high quality work on group projects, and be prepared to do a great deal of supervision, but in general this will be a very cheap option—the exceptions are some of the more prestigious business schools which charge near commercial rates for their postgraduate project work.

10.26 Individual faculty members may also be prepared to take on a piece of research and form an ad hoc research team (see the section on commissioning). And higher education institutions often keep registers of ex-students and others who have particular research skills, such as interviewing, and are available for employment on a temporary basis.

The Kings Fund[1]

10.27 The King's Fund no longer provide packs of questionnaires, but their library holds individual copies of all their questionnaires, associated reports and many other studies. The Fund may also be able to give some limited advice on conducting a survey, but at present cannot offer a full support service.

Health Policy Advisory Unit

10.28 The UMIST questionnaire and an entire survey and analysis package was until recently available from HPAU in Sheffield. The Unit is currently (Nov.1988) homeless, but will reply to postal enquiries at their Sheffield P.O.Box.[2] Other enquiries regarding surveys and survey design can also be directed to Andy Thompson,[3] who may be able to arrange help with conducting surveys.

Notes

1. The Kings Fund Centre for Health Services Development, 126 Albert Street, London NW1 7NF (01–267–6111).
2. Health Policy Advisory Unit, P.O.Box 344, Sheffield S1 1AZ.
3. Dr.A.Thompson, University of Wales, College of Cardiff, Aberconway Building, Colum Rd, Cardiff CF1 3EU (0222 342588x2105).

GLOSSARY

For further explanation of these terms see paragraphs referred to in parentheses.

Basic Frequency count: the numbers of observations in the data which fall into each category of a particular variable (8.6–8.14).

Canonical Analysis: a form of multivariate analysis where the predictor variables are recombined into the smallest set of 'orthoginal' variables—that is, variables which vary independently of each other—which best predict the dependent variable.

Clustering: can either refer to a method of sampling or a technique of analysis. Here the reference is to a sampling procedure whereby the target sample is grouped into relatively small geographical areas for ease of interviewing. If carried out properly, a clustered sample can still be statistically respectable (3.22).

Chi-squared test: a test as to whether an observed series of frequencies differ between themselves, or from a series of frequencies expected on some hypotheses, to a greater degree than might be expected to occur by chance (8.42–8.45).

Coding sheets: specially designed forms for entering data derived from the answers to a questionnaire (or from another source) prior to transcription into a computer data file (7.15–7.17).

Contingency table: is the general term for a two-way classification specifying varying numbers of discrete categories in each of two dimensions (8.37–8.39).

Critical incident analysis: is a method of investigation. The central feature is the reconstruction by the patient of her or his hospital or other care experiences. Patients are asked especially to report anything which seemed to them important, notable, strange or worrying (1.8–1.11).

Cross-sectional design: a research design aiming to take a snapshot of conditions at a particular moment (2.19–2.20).

Cross tabulation: a tabulation of the data from a survey according to the responses to two specific variables, showing how the responses to one question are related to the responses to another (8.37–8.39).

Direct entry: transcription of the data directly from the questionnaire on to a computer data file (7.18–7.20).

Factor Analysis: a form of multivariate analysis which provides a representation of one, large, set of variables by another, smaller (usually much smaller) set.

Filtering: the route which respondents should follow through the questionnaire. Sometimes varies according to who they are; more often according to the responses they give (4.19–4.21).

Indexation: transforming the answers to a question (or set of questions) into a single index number (8.21–8.26).

Index values: the simplest kind of index number is the value index. It compares total value in some period with total value in the base period. For example, an index of department stores sales would be a value index. Total value would be a sum of the price of each item times the number sold. This type of index is seldom used because it is difficult to determine just what changes it measures. If the index rises, one is not sure whether it has risen because of a price increase or because of an increase in volume. It may be the result of both. The same is true for any other combination of different items (8.21–8.26).

Multi-stage designs: it is rarely possible or practicable to draw a simple random sample directly from the entire target population. More typically the process of sampling involves several different stages with, often, different principles of selection (3.21).

Numerical weights: these are used in analysis either to correct for potential bias introduced by the sampling method (see Chapter 3) or to combine the responses from different questions to produce an index number (8.26).

Precoded questions/data: questions where the possible answers have been defined before the questionnaire was administered. They are often but not necessarily read out to the respondent to 'force' her choice (7.6–7.7).

Proxy List: where there is no suitable list of the target population, an alternative to the time-consuming process of constructing your own, is to ask the interviewers to define who should have been on the list, as they are carrying out the fieldwork (3.35).

Pseudo-Random number generation routine: a computer software package which generates a list of random numbers which can be used for sampling.

Quota sampling method: is a form of purposive sampling widely used in opinion, market, and similar surveys. The enumerates are instructed to obtain specified quotas from which to build a sample roughly proportional to the population, on a few demographic variables. Within the quotas, the enumerates are supposed to obtain representative individuals. The nature of the controls and instructions depend on the expert judgement of the practitioner (3.39–3.44).

Randomised Control Trial (RCT): a rare event in this area of research: the conditions for an RCT are not applicable (2.30).

Simple Random Sampling: drawing a sample from a universe (or parent population) by a random method, e.g. by the use of random sampling numbers, which gives any individual in the universe an equal and independent chance of appearing in the sample (3.17).

Stratification: a method of increasing the representation of groups who might otherwise be excluded from any analysis, and of making the most use of the resources available for the survey (3.19–3.21).

BIBLIOGRAPHY

(A) Reports of patient feedback studies

Barking, Havering & Brentwood (83) CHC "A & E Studies, Oldchurch Hospital"

Brent (86) "Health Care in Brent"

Cambridge (84) CHC with Cambridge University "Survey of Waiting Times in Out-Patient Department, Addenbrookes Hospital"

East Dorset (87) CHC "Survey of Out-Patients Needs & Priorities, Christchurch Hospital"

Exeter (82) CHC "Medical Services in Rural Areas"

Gregory J *Patients Attitudes to the Hospital Service: A Survey Carried Out for the Royal Commission on the NHS* Research Paper no 5 London HMSO

Haran D, Elkind A K & Eardley A "Consulting the Consumers"

(83A) *Health and Social Service Journal* Nov 3 1983

(83B) *Health and Social Service Journal* Nov 10 1983

Macclesfield (85) CHC "Survey of Out-Patients Choices in Macclesfield District, April/May 1985"

Maidstone (87) HA & University of Kent "An Apple A Day ...? A Study of Lifestyles and Health in Maidstone"

North East Essex (87) HA, Standards Department "Out-Patient Department Survey"

North Western Region (82) "North West Regional Study of A & E Services" (Authors—Yvonne Bradbury & Barbara Lewis [UMIST])

Northumberland (82) CHC "Seaton Sluice—A Survey of Health Facilities"

North East Essex (88) HA, Standards Department CHC "Mixed Sex Wards"

North West Thames RHA
    (86A) "Managing Customer Relations—Taking a Snapshot
    (86B) "Managing Customer Relations"
    (86C) "Managing Customer Relations—The Customer's Agenda"

Raphel W
    (69) "Patients and Their Hospitals" 1st Edition
    (77) "Patients and Their Hospitals" 3rd Edition
    (72) "Psychiatric Hospitals Viewed by Their Patients"
    (79) "Old People in Hospital"

Sunderland (85) CHC "Ambulance Survey—Non-Emergency Service"

Southport & Formby (87) HA "Out-Patient Survey"

Southmead (88) HA "Survey into Waiting Times at the A & E Department"

Swindon (88) HA "Investigations into Patient Satisfaction with A & E Department"

Shefield (78) CHC "Difficulties and Needs of Ethnic Minority Groups"

Salisbury (88) HA "Consumer Survey 1987"

Tower Hamlets (84) Department of Community Medicine "The Spitalfields Health Survey"

Warrington (87) CHC "Survey into Visiting Arrangements at the District General Hospital"

Warrington (85) CHC "Survey of Out-Patient Clinics at Warrington District General Hospital"

Wirral (86) CHC & Liverpool University "Survey into A & E. Attendances at Arrow Park Hospital

Wolverhampton (88) CHE (York) "Report on Health in Wolverhampton"

Warrington (84) CHC & HA "Patients Opinion Survey at Warrington District General Hospital"

Waltham Forest (86) CHC "Carers—A Report"

Worthing (77) CHC "Concern for the Elderly"

(B) Texts and articles on research methods

Cartwright A (88) *Health Surveys in practice and potential*

French K (81) *Methodological considerations in hospital patient opinon surveys*

Gardiner G *Social Surveys for Social Planners* M Keynes 1978 Jahoda et al (65) *Research Methods and Social Relations*

Jones et al (87) *Consumer Feedback for the NHS: A Literature Review*

McCrossan (84) *A Handbook for Interviewers*

Mosser & Kalton (71) *Survey Methods in Social Investigation*

Oakley A (80) *Women Confined : Towards a Sociology of Childbirth*

Oakley A (81) "Interviewing Women : A Contradiction in Terms" in *Doing Feminist Research* H Roberts (ed)

Oppenheim *Questionnaire Design and Attitude Measurement*

Payne *Art of Asking Questions*

Survey Research Centre at the University of Michigan (70) *Interviewers Manual*

Wilmott P & Young M (57) *Family and Kinship in East London*